Eve

death, berea

through the eyes of children, parents
and practitioners

For Kate, Ben, Sally and Amy,
whose lives have enriched mine
more than they will ever know…

…and for every young life that
briefly touched mine
and left an indelible mark

Everylife:
death, bereavement and life through the eyes of children, parents and practitioners

by Shirley Potts

APS Publishing

APS Publishing
The Old School, Tollard Royal, Salisbury, Wiltshire, SP5 5PW
www.apspublishing.co.uk

British Library Cataloguing in Publication Data
A catalogue record for this book is available from the British Library

© APS Publishing 2005
ISBN 1 9038772 6 1

Printed in the United Kingdom by Cromwell Press, Trowbridge,
Wiltshire.

Cover photograph:
Sherriff Studios
66 Eastbank Street, Southport
PR8 1ES
www.sherriffstudios.co.uk

Contents

Acknowledgements

I am indebted to many people who have informed, influenced or encouraged this book. First and foremost, of course, to the families and staff of Derian House Children's Hospice, without whom the book would not exist and my life experience would be sadly diminished. The opportunity to work with colleagues of such exceptional calibre and families of such diverse experience has transformed my professional understanding and changed my personal outlook irrevocably. It would be easy to idealise, or even romanticise, children's hospice work and I am inclined to be effusive in my endorsement of its practitioners—but let that not detract from the skilled and compassionate provision that these places offer to families in need.

I would like to specifically thank Mike Farrell for his foresight and faith in appointing me to the newly created post of Family Support Co-ordinator at Derian House, and supporting the innovations the staff and I devised.

My thanks also to Professor Gavin Fairbairn for assisting my route to publication, and to colleagues at Liverpool Hope University College who have encouraged me along the way, and to Valery Marston of APS Publishing whose temperate communications have alleviated some of the pressures of deadline commitments.

I must offer apologies and gratitude to my family and friends who have tolerated both my presence and my absence during a year of writing.

Finally, I acknowledge the impact on my life of Margaret Jolliffe, David Goodwin and Prue Dufour, whose dying taught me more about living.

Introduction

'A sigh is something your heart says that your head doesn't understand'

That statement, which introduces the second section of this book, was from a prematurely wise six-year-old bereaved brother who triggered my resolve to record some of the heart and head knowledge acquired and enhanced through the years I spent in the role of Family Support Co-ordinator at Derian House Children's Hospice in Lancashire, UK.

This book is offered not only for the edification of practitioners in the field of bereavement, but primarily as a debt of honour to a number of children and families whose lives touched mine. Those who experience the death of a child tread a path that is at once well worn yet unique to them. There is a need to hear their voices because doing so can validate the lives of those who have died, and illuminate the quest for meaning that their surviving families seek. Moreover, listening to the voices of those who have lived closely with death can alert professionals to the significance of their own humanity—with a reminder that a practitioner's humanity, as much as their wisdom, is brought into encounters with the bereaved or dying. For many years, there has been a prevailing belief that professionals bring skill, support and expertise to these situations, perpetuating the mythical power imbalance between those with needs and those with solutions. In truth, practitioners are (or should be) changed, enlightened and mellowed through their encounters with the dying and bereaved.

A life, and a death, makes an impact upon the world. However small the impact, however brief the life, there is a ripple effect that continues—and countless lives are touched.

The content of this book reflects the reality of death as a fact of life, and survival as the most likely outcome for bereaved families. Survival… we can see the root words sur and vive—'to live on'. Not necessarily implying the 'don't look back/escapism' survival, but living on as one might live on a main road, or live on a mountain. The journey to that survival and the changes of outlook along the way merit chronicling—not only, if at all, to proffer advice to those who may yet have to experience bereavement, but also to remind the many, who feel safely cocooned from death and tragedy, that no life, since time began, has been untouched by death (hence the title). We can give increasing value to life as we set it in the respectful context of death.

The book is in three sections, offering three quite different perceptions of the experience of years lived within the context of child death.

The first section incorporates theoretical perspectives, giving an overview of how we got to where we are with models of grief; societal and cultural changes; counselling approaches and the radical reappraisals of the last two decades. In addition to a closer examination of three specific counselling approaches that I found particularly relevant to bereavement support, there is a summary of children's developmental cognition of death in relation to their chronological or emotional age, and some suggestions for school-based bereavement support.

The second section contains the practical and experiential outcomes of seven years spent working at Derian House Children's Hospice, devising, initiating and sustaining bereavement support for all generations of families. This period included hundreds of conversations, counselling exchanges and other communication with bereaved parents and children, that offered me a well of pragmatic advice from which I regularly drew. Patently, there were also many encounters with dying children and their insights and perceptions deserve recording. During this time I also undertook a research project examining the narrative constructs of bereaved parents, and this too will be expounded. In discussing the families who utilised the hospice, I have made a comprehensive decision to avoid all real names—those present in the text are substitutions. This was not as straightforward as it sounds as I was aware from my research with bereaved parents that some parents were diametrically opposed to me giving their dead child a pseudonym—and thus 'diminishing' the reality of that child's existence. Others prefer anonymity, and to them I acquiesce, in the hope that any who recognise themselves, or are recognised by others, within the pages of this book will appreciate the invaluable contribution they have made to our expanding understanding of child death and bereavement support.

The book concludes with a very personal perspective. I am very aware that the years at Derian House permanently changed my own values and outlook—and it would seem disrespectful not to conclude with a reflection on that impact, those who wrought it, and their continuing influence on my life.

The sections almost stand alone, but it is hoped the book in its entirety will contribute to the ongoing debate around the changing face of palliative care and bereavement support.

Section I

Theoretical Perspectives

1

Setting the scene

A wander through the literature on death and bereavement over the last century draws some interesting paradoxes. There was a united outcry from social commentators during the 1960s and '70s that death had become a 'taboo' (Aries, 1981; Gorer, 1965; Simpson, 1979; Walter, 1991), even though Simpson commented, after having collected a bibliography of publications in English about death, that 'there are over 650 books now in print asserting that we are ignoring the subject'. This offers one paradox. Can a topic that is so widely promulgated really be a taboo subject? Shortly after his cleverly titled *'Taboo or not taboo?'* (Walter, 1991), Walter introduced a further suggestion of the 'revival of death' (Walter, 1994).

Since that time death and bereavement have been increasingly researched and written about. If we look further back to the beginnings of the twentieth century we find that death and mourning were much more public proceedings. The deceased lay, open to the view of respectful visitors, in the parlour of the Victorian home awaiting a ritualised, sombre journey to their final resting place (Aries, 1981). Mourners were clearly identifiable by their dress and standardised periods of time were ascribed to their grief. Even children participated in the proceedings and there are elderly people who today recall the experience—or trauma—of having an open coffin in their childhood home. That practice has not entirely disappeared, but is certainly less common.

It would appear that the period of 'death as taboo' was, in fact the thirty or forty post-war years that led to the era sociologists might call late modernity. More recent literature expounds a post-modern approach to death and bereavement with less rigid adherence to the dictates of theorists and a more flexible acknowledgement of the uniqueness of each individual and their approach to dying or mourning. However, that is not to eradicate or underestimate the contributions of former influences and it is necessary to examine the journey so far in order to appreciate our current location. It is also worth mentioning at this point (although the issue will be scrutinised in more depth in Section II) that the lived experience of the general populace is some way behind the proclamations of essayists and critics in the field. There are, indeed, those who would still affirm the isolating effects of grief and mourning, and the classic experience of seeing acquaintances cross the road rather than struggle with an encounter with a bereaved person, has not vanished, only lessened.

Major histories of death in Britain and the Western world are available for those who require an even longer view (Aries, 1981; Jupp and Gittings, 1999; Levinas, 2000; Walter, 1999) and make fascinating reading, but for the purpose of this discussion, I will examine changes during the last century.

Prior to 1900 one quarter of all deaths were children, with those figures only diminishing in the early twentieth century as deaths from infectious diseases began to decline. There is a popular conception that Victorian parents were philosophical about the anticipated loss and therefore reduced their emotional investment in their children. This is more likely to be a concept conceived and held by societies several decades removed from the reality. I have to confess to at one time succumbing to the tidy notion that a greater frequency of child death must have made the anguish more tolerable for former generations. In fact, I used to relay this concept to the current generation of bereaved parents in the hope that it would reflect my empathy with their exceptional grief. The words of John Tittensor, an Australian writer who lost his two children in a house fire, chastised me:

> 'As their first anniversary approaches, I remind myself that it is only in our own time that people have come to expect their children to live to maturity as a matter of course. My own mother was one of six children, two of whom became ill and died within the first year of their lives; in the 1920s this wasn't regarded as exceptional. The only trouble: this knowledge is no consolation whatsoever.'
>
> (McCracken and Semel, 1998)

4

There is much evidence that the death of a child in Victorian times was as painful to parents then as it is now. The statistics may have altered beyond all recognition over the past one hundred years, but the desolation of child loss was, and is, immeasurable. The Victorian family did, however, have the support structures of religion, ritual and remembrance. Romanticist perceptions of grief had largely prevailed to include the Victorian era. Contrary to the breaking bonds orientation of modernism, romanticism upheld sustaining connections with the deceased—despite a 'broken heart'. Grief gave external confirmation of the depth of a relationship. Therefore to sever memories of the deceased implied a shallowness and superficiality to the relationship and a lack of depth in the griever (Stroebe *et al*, 1992). There is a wealth of paintings, sculptures, stained glass, prose and poetry from that era dedicated to beloved family members who have died.

If I edge somewhat beyond the past hundred years of my focus, we find this romanticist view clearly illustrated in a tender poem of William Wordsworth, best known for his wanderings amongst daffodils. Yet he, too, was a bereaved father whose heart ached over the loss of his four-year-old daughter, Catherine, in 1812:

'Surprised by joy—impatient as the wind
I turned to share the transport—Oh! With whom
But thee, deep buried in the silent tomb,
That spot which no vicissitude can find?
Love, faithful love, recalled thee to my mind—
But how could I forget thee? Through what power,
Even for the least division of an hour,
Have I been so beguiled as to be blind
To my most grievous loss! That thought's return
Was the worst pang that sorrow ever bore,
Save one, one only, when I stood forlorn,
Knowing my heart's best treasure was no more;
That neither present time, nor years unborn
Could to my sight that heavenly face restore.'

(Harmon, 1992)

Nevertheless, while the pain of parental loss may remain the same through the centuries—and any categorisation or measurement of such pain would be fruitless anyway—the surrounding circumstances have altered radically over time. As previously stated, the Victorians still had the support structures incumbent in religion, ritual and remembrance. For the current generation, these have diminished substantially. As an increasingly secular society, only a small proportion of the current population would acknowledge the sustenance of a religious faith, whereas Victorian England was still regarded, nominally at least, as a largely Christian society. Belief in an afterlife brought comfort; the church and offices of death framed the familiar rituals that gave families a sense of structure as they grappled with the disorientation of grief; friends and supporters knew how to behave and respond through time-honoured tradition and the polite but comforting formalities of condolence. Clocks were stopped, curtains drawn, clothing dictated, prayers recited, and although we may assume an air of supercilious and sophisticated post-modern disdain for such rituals, we have, perhaps, travelled a little too far in distancing ourselves from those responses to death. These days, many attendees at funerals in churches are likely to shuffle uncomfortably, be unsure of when to enter and where to sit and mumble awkwardly through any hymns or prayers. So here we have another paradox—the proclaimed freedoms of our permissive, progressive society leave us, in some situations, agonisingly liberated with such a dearth of boundaries that we have no sense of direction or security.

Is this progress? Or is it a mere staging point on our endless journey towards an understanding of death and our response to it?

Philippe Aries' seminal work on a history of death (1981) offers similar comparisons between the beginnings of the twentieth century and the Thatcher years of the eighties:

> 'Today, a complete reversal of customs seems to have occurred... In my youth, women in mourning were invisible under their crepe and voluminous black veils. Middle class children whose grandmothers had died were dressed in violet.
>
> Except for the death of statesmen, society has banished

death. In the towns, there is no way of knowing that something has happened... Society no longer observes a pause; the disappearance of an individual no longer affects its continuity. Everything in town goes on as if nobody died anymore.'

In the wider historical context, this change in approach has been so rapid as to jolt sociologists, philosophers and others into a consideration of these remarkable phenomena. Thus we have the relatively brief period where death became taboo, but then reappeared as a topic under much scrutiny and discussion. As Aries predicted, 'Shown the door by society, death is coming back in through the window, and it is returning just as quickly as it disappeared.'

The medicalisation of death

Until the middle of the twentieth century, it was far more likely that dying and death would take place in the home rather than the hospital. The dying were 'sent home to die' when the hospital could offer no further treatment. Family members, for the most part, handled the unpalatable elements of caring for a dying, deteriorating body, not only out of love, but because they had no option. That century was also an era of rapid development and changing perceptions in our knowledge of personal and public hygiene, asepsis and contagion. By the end of the twentieth century, the UK population were, by and large, far less willing or able to tolerate the sights and smells of death to which their ancestors at the start of the century would have been accustomed.

Undoubtedly, two world wars had a tremendous impact on attitudes to death and the rituals surrounding it (Gorer, 1965). Time-honoured traditions had to give way to the pressing, emergency situation of women working in what were formerly regarded as men's roles, while men in the armed forces died in unprecedented numbers far from home. It is not surprising, therefore, that this century witnessed such startlingly rapid changes in the culture of death, dying and bereavement.

This introduces a further paradox. The evolution of palliative care and the hospice movement has heralded the possibility of a return to death at home. In some circumstances, it has become possible for the dying patient to receive palliative care and pain control via the hospice, but also have the services of home care, such as Macmillan or Marie Curie nurses, and choose to die at home, if preferred. This is particularly true of the children's hospice movement where families might feel more able to care for a sick or dying child in their home environment, with some professional support. One of the watchwords of the post-modern age is 'choice' and this is the major difference between the start and end of the twentieth century. Many families—and this will be discussed in more depth later—dread the thought of a family member dying at home and prefer the comforting surroundings of calm professionalism. There are no right or wrongs here, and I feel it is an area where choice, when possible, is one of the few consolations we can afford our dying and their families.

The Hospice Movement

The original meaning of hospice in mediaeval times was a resting place for weary travellers, perhaps not so far removed from today's concept. The first hospice for the dying was probably that opened in 1842 by Jeanne Garnier, of 'Les Dames du Calvaire' in France. This innovation was led mainly by women of religious orientation and was a philanthropic venture that cared for the dying soul as much as the dying body. These were the origins of holistic care, and while the religious ministrations may have diminished at the dawn of a twenty-first century, we owe a debt of gratitude to those forerunners who perceived terminal care as an opportunity to attend to the whole person (Clark and Seymour, 2002).

This concept was spearheaded in the UK by Dame Cicely Saunders who is credited with initiating the hospice movement that we see today. In 1948 she nursed a terminally ill patient, a young man by the name of David Tasma who, when offered whatever medical comfort was available, responded, 'I only want what is in your heart and in your mind'. From conversations with this young man, Cicely Saunders appreciated the spiritual, emotional and psychological needs of the dying, as well as their physical care, and vowed to open the country's first hospice. Beginning with £500 left to her by David Tasma ('I'll be a window in your hospice'), she fundraised persistently and St Christopher's Hospice in London opened in 1967 (where there is, indeed, a window dedicated to David Tasma).

Rarely has a movement expanded with such speed and there are now hospices in most large towns and cities of the UK. Some maintain a religious orientation, some are NHS establishments, but the majority are voluntary funded, independent organisations that rely for the most part on public donations. Legacies from former patients form a substantial part of those donations, a custom that is understandably not echoed within the children's hospice movement.

Hospices for children are an even more recent innovation, beginning in 1982 with the opening of Helen House in Oxford. Its founder, Sister Frances Dominica, had come to realise that there was no appropriate place for dying children between hospital and home. Hospital, while still the environment where the largest number of child deaths occurs, has its limitations; the sterile and clinical setting may not be the preferred place for families. (The high incidence of hospital-based child deaths is not related to terminal care, it is simply because the main cause of death in childhood is trauma-related conditions.) Home, however, is equally limited in its lack of medical and professional support at a time when families' coping skills are undermined by their anxieties and heartache. So, starting with Helen House and evolving into a movement that now includes about thirty establishments or projects throughout the UK, the children's hospice became the halfway house between hospital and home.

It is worth explaining at this point some of the many differences, and some similarities, between adult and child hospice care. Adult hospices cared almost entirely for cancer patients, although recent years have seen the criteria broaden to encompass conditions such as motor neurone disease and other terminal diseases. There is ongoing debate within the adult hospice movement regarding the increasing breadth of admission criteria, but that debate is not the concern of this book. In contrast, children's hospices always had a much wider remit. This is in accordance with the kinds of conditions from which children die. Essentially, the criteria for utilising the services of a children's hospice are that the child has a life-threatening or life-limiting condition. Put simply, the child is not expected to survive into adulthood although some conditions may have an unpredictable outcome. Thus, the overwhelming bed-occupancy of a children's hospice is respite care, although, when it arises, terminal care will always take priority. However, for the most part, families will utilise the facilities of a children's hospice to give themselves, and their child, temporary relief and support during the arduous journey of a child's illness.

Children's hospices will encounter neurodegenerative diseases such as Batten's disease; metabolic disorders such as mucopolysaccharides diseases or the mitochondrial diseases; neuro-muscular conditions such as Duchenne Muscular Dystrophy; and numerous other rare disorders, whose rarity corroborates the limited research opportunities of a limited life span.

Between 10 and 20 per cent of children's hospice users may be cancer patients—a much smaller percentage than in adult hospice care—reflecting both the curative possibilities of childhood cancers, and also the lower incidence comparatively within the child population. While children being treated for cancer (most often leukaemia or brain tumours) may clearly have a life-threatening condition and thereby qualify for hospice care, many families would not wish to avail themselves of that support, even temporarily, given the historical morbid associations with the word 'hospice'. Hope for cure is an important factor in paediatric oncology and, in contrast with the adult hospices, this particular client group is notably the most wary of the children's hospice environment—at least until family members have accommodated the sad and difficult prognosis that, for their child, curative treatment is no longer an option.

Contrary to popular belief, children's hospices are cheerful, brightly decorated environments. The facilities are generous, encompassing provisions, such as outdoor play areas, indoor soft-play areas, art rooms, music rooms, hydrotherapy pools, computer equipment, lounge areas and attractive gardens, as well as, of course , the requisite medical facilities. Needless to say, as with many adult hospices, medicalisation of the environment is minimal. While many hospices are leading the field in pain control and other elements of palliative care, they are at pains to offer more homely surroundings than are possible within a hospital. Most children's hospices will also offer family accommodation as many families are reluctant to leave their sick child. There, are, however, those occasions of respite care where a family may take the opportunity to take a break from caring—albeit to decorate a bedroom or focus on other siblings—or when children themselves, particularly adolescents, might welcome the semi-independence of a brief period away from their solicitous family. The staff team reflects the breadth of the facilities, incorporating highly trained children's nurses as well as general nurses, healthcare assistants, housekeeping staff and administrative staff, together with the invaluable armies of volunteers who do so much to support the funding and day-to-day running of hospices. Many children's hospices will have additional therapies available, such as physiotherapy, music therapy and art therapy. My own role as Family Support Co-ordinator, responsible for counselling and bereavement support, was the first full-time post of that nature within children's hospice, but is now, gratifyingly, much more widespread. There is a popular dictum within children's hospice that dying children 'have a lot of living to do' and this is especially true for those whose allotted lifespan is likely to be briefer than one would normally hope. Children's hospices are places for living, as much as dying, and places of laughter as well as tears.

Theories of grief

Freud (1917) may be largely responsible for the later, pervasive intimations of closure and completion for the bereaved, for he believed the function of mourning was to 'detach the survivor's hopes and memories from the dead'. To put this statement in its fuller context, it is apparent that Freud was rather less dogmatic in his considerations of grief. It would be a harsh assessment of Freud to assume he propagated closure and little else. His first case, drawing him into a lifelong study of melancholia, was a young woman expressing symptoms of grief after the death of her father. Freud comments: 'there is certainly nothing pathological in being fixated to the memory of a dead person so short a time after his decease; on the contrary it would be a normal emotional process' (Freud, 1910). Thus the father of psychoanalysis concurred with the experience of countless generations—that mourning is a necessary process in normal healthy living. It was, in fact, this initial patient who called her analysis 'the talking cure' unwittingly predicting the basis of many a counselling theory yet to be established and coining a phrase that fell into common parlance. Freud did distinguish between healthy mourning and pathological grief, with its subsequent melancholia or depression, asserting that the inability to detach from grief and 'move on' was symptomatic of sickness.

Detachment and severance have been recurrent themes in subsequent theories of grief and loss. It is not difficult to understand the emotive basis of such theories. Many unpleasant experiences in life have, historically, been advised as being best forgotten, moved on from, left behind and undisturbed. Grief has been characterised, amid much criticism, as an illness (Engel, 1961) with its inevitable connotations of 'recovery'. But undoubtedly it is the psychology, rather than the physiology, of grief that has drawn the most theoretical attention.

Within the ample literature pertaining to death, dying and bereavement, Bowlby's seminal work (Bowlby, 1969) on separation and loss remains a classic foundational tenet. His observed psychological progression in children temporarily abandoned by their mother is as relevant in grief as it was in maternal deprivation. He observed in many instances the child's progression through protestation, despair and detachment and we must be grateful to him for the radical improvements for hospitalised children who are now separated as little as possible from the comforting presence of a parent. Unfortunately, Bowlby's conclusions were transferred somewhat crudely into bereavement theories at times, with detachment being the concluding phase of several subsequent models.

Parkes' (1972) studies of bereavement in the 1960s and 1970s brought a new dimension to bereavement research, and he was one of the first proponents of a series of stages the bereaved must work through. From Freud, he took the idea of griefwork and outlined the stages of grief through which mourners should pass.

- Shock, numbness and disbelief
- Pain, grief, sadness, anger or guilt
- Desolation, despair and full realisation
- Re-involvement in life and a new identity.

Worden's *Grief Counselling and Grief Therapy* (Worden, 1988) has similarly become a classic and his four tasks of grieving have been the standard basis for many training courses in bereavement counselling:

- Task 1: to accept the reality of the loss
- Task 2: to experience the pain of grief
- Task 3: to adjust to life without the deceased
- Task 4: to relocate emotional energy elsewhere.

I have personally undertaken training that was centred on these tenets little more than a decade ago, which might dismay Parkes and Worden as both have since revisited their models and modified them somewhat according to experiential practice and practitioner research. As I stated earlier, protagonists in the field are reviewing and softening former rigid models (or models that were interpreted rigidly) but the lived experience of the general populace is that their friends, family and, dare I say, even their counsellors on occasion, have not yet revised an understanding of grief that belongs to former decades. A cursory reading of earlier Worden has sometimes ill-equipped enthusiastic amateurs to proclaim to their unfortunate bereaved friends or relatives that they are 'in denial', or 'experiencing task three'.

I did have an instinctive dissatisfaction with Worden's fourth task, implying as it did a measuring out of emotional energy that had to be reapportioned when death occurred. My intuitive response was that, ideally, just as parents love each child no less when subsequent children are born, then nor do they need to withdraw their emotional investment on the death of a child? Unquestionably, the physicality and structure of their family are drastically redefined, but emotional connectedness surely continues?

One can, however, understand the appeal of closure and detachment to those who helplessly watch friend, relative or client battle with the anguish of incurable grief. Helplessness is one of the most miserable of human states and no doubt the cause of many road-crossings in the avoidance of a bereaved person. In spite of the appeal of 'recovery', 'closure', ' detachment' and so on, such recommendations are essentially flawed. The human mind has not yet acquired the capacity to consciously forget. In the case of parents bereaved of a child, statements such as 'put it behind you' and 'let go and move on' are anathema to them. Not only are such feats of consciousness beyond the remit of the human psyche, but equally parents are offended and bemused by the suggestion that they should want to forget their child. Such suggestions only serve to confirm the inadequacies of the supporters. If a hurting person is advised to put the source of their pain 'behind' them, are we subconsciously expressing our own intolerance to their insoluble pain? Is the construct inherent in that statement, 'please put your pain where I cannot see it'?

In the cultural context of the mid to late-eighties, challenges to fixed models or patterns of grief were emerging. Wortman and Silver (1989) suggested that some bereaved people, most particularly parents bereaved of a child, may never find meaning in the death. Recovery, completion, closure and resolution are unhelpful terms for bereaved parents.

To reiterate a defence of Parkes and Worden, both they and other theorists stress that the grieving process is never as tidy as a series of tasks or stages might suggest. Wortman *et al* (1999) affirm this point in their contributory chapter in the *Handbook of Bereavement*, (Stroebe *et al*, 1993);

> '...and because of the lack of evidence in support of them, there is growing speculation that these models may not be as useful as previously believed. In fact, the authoritative review of bereavement research issued by the Institute of Medicine cautioned against the use of the term "stages" of response.'

These merely outline symptomology that might well be observed in mourners, but different phases may reappear or be missed entirely. Grieving is more of a scribble than a straight line. Indeed,

Worden's theoretical progression through tasks has been modified over time, with stipulations that the tasks can be revisited or appear out of sequence. In the second edition of Worden's book (Worden, 1991), he modified his final stage to:

- Finding an appropriate place for the deceased in the bereaved person's emotional life.

In his more recent work, *Children and Grief* (Worden, 1996), it is apparent that Worden has moved experientially from the more structured tasks of his initial theory to a more flexible, individualised and compassionate approach—perhaps exemplified by his choice of co-workers in this project, specifically Phyllis Silverman. Worden states:

> *'The task facing the bereaved is not to give up the relationship with the deceased but to find a new and appropriate place for the dead in their emotional lives—one that enables them to go on living effectively in the world.'*

Children and Grief is an exposition of the results of a longitudinal study—the Harvard Child Bereavement Study—that included extensive interviews with bereaved children and families. Worden's associates in this undertaking were Phyllis Silvermann and Steven Nickman who were, in turn, collaborators with Denis Klass in editing *Continuing Bonds* (Klass *et al*, 1996), a milestone in bereavement literature which espouses a paradigm of ongoing connectedness between bereaved and deceased.

Elizabeth Kubler-Ross (1970) heralded the innovative approach of physicians listening to the narrative of their dying patients and their families. For some time, she was a lone voice in the midst of a clinical, sanitised establishment and her books carried less academic weight than others. Nevertheless, her pioneering practice of narrative intervention with her dying and bereaved patients set standards that are foundational to the current changes in approaches to bereavement. Still, she, too, succumbed to the tacit expectation of producing a suggested route through dying or grief. For Kubler-Ross, these were not tasks, but stages.

- First stage: denial and isolation

- Second stage: anger
- Third stage: bargaining
- Fourth stage: depression
- Fifth stage: acceptance.

Sheldon (Sheldon, 1997) ruminates:

> *'Just as the widespread acceptance of the ideas of Elizabeth Kubler-Ross may well have been because they helped professionals to contain their sense of chaos and despair in the face of death, so, too, a model of bereavement which suggests that the outcome of this painful process is acceptance and detachment from the deceased, gave a feeling of order and relief to those alongside the bereaved. Similarly, this may again have led to an over-simplification of the original ideas as they seeped into practice.'*

So, while our major exponents of grief theory have adapted their theories in the light of broadening understanding and knowledge, there still tends to be a time-lapse between such discoveries and society's absorption of them in practice.

One of the most articulate and astute proponents of current grief theory is Maggie Stroebe (Stroebe and Schut, 1998; Stroebe and Schut, 1995; Stroebe *et al*, 1993; Stroebe, 1992; Stroebe *et al*, 1992). Her Dual-Process model of coping with loss has presented a challenging alternative to earlier, linear models and certainly coincides with the experience of many of the families with whom I worked. The Dual-Process model is characterised by an 'oscillation' on the part of the griever between 'loss-orientation' and 'restoration-orientation'. Stroebe and Schut assert that this oscillation represents normal, healthy grieving, where the griever may experience episodes of profound sadness yet also takes 'time-out' from grieving, using distraction and temporary avoidance through other activities.

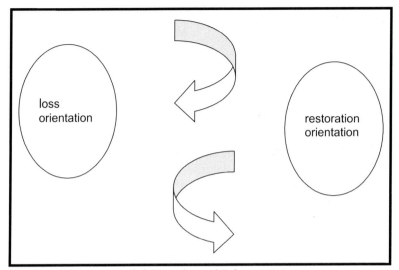

The Dual-Process model (Stroebe and Schut, 1995)

This model is particularly accessible to those who are bereaved, for they know only too well that episodes of incapacitating sorrow are nevertheless interspersed with the mundane trivia of life, like brushing teeth or filling the kettle. Additionally, there are those times when bereaved people might consciously enter into avoidant activities as temporary respite from their emotional pain, actions often misinterpreted as denial. I recall a perceptive conference presentation by Richard Obershaw where he evidenced that 'denial is acceptance' (Obershaw, 1999), citing an occasion where he had unfortunately hit a dog while driving along a country road. He reflected that as he pulled over and steadfastly refused to raise his eyes to his rear-view mirror, all too aware of what he would see lying in the road, he was thinking 'I didn't hit that dog did I?' We can recognise in that the acknowledgement and acceptance that often accompany the apparently contradictory words of our lips. Jim Kuykendall reminds us that in Gestalt work this would be termed 'creative adjustment' and he speaks of 'the wonderful gift of denial' (Kuykendall, 1998). This is consistent with Rogers' concept of subception (Carl Rogers initiated the person-centred counselling approach), where the client adaptively adjusts experiences in order to deny or inaccurately perceive those elements which are inconsistent with the 'actualising tendency'—Rogers' term for healthy progression towards optimum growth and potential (Nelson-Jones, 1995).

Increasingly, grief is perceived as a 'complex and evolving process requiring the use of a multidimensional model' (Raphael *et al*, 1993). Paul Rosenblatt has contributed helpfully to these dimensions with his research interviews with bereaved parents, adopting a very similar approach to my own research (Rosenblatt, 2000a; b). He notes that the occasional use of present tense by parents when talking of a deceased child is rarely indicative of pathological grief or any connotations with denial. Rather it is mostly a manifestation of the cultural principles grounded in ways of thinking that are widespread in North American (and northern European) culture. He identifies the following five principles:

- Parent and child continue to have a relationship

- The child has a spiritual existence in the present

- The child exists in the present in some location

- Things that belonged to the child remain the child's

- Death does not necessarily end a child's personal or social characteristics.

(Rosenblatt, 2000b)

When Klass, Silverman and Nickman produced *Continuing Bonds*, they were at pains to emphasise that they were not peddling yet another model onto the market, but were airing the debate around continuance as opposed to closure or detaching (Klass *et al*, 1996). Their stance within the debate was clear, not only from the title of the volume, but also in its content. Their suggestion was a model of grieving that integrates 'the complexity of human relationships and the ways in which people remain connected to each other in life and in death.'

Within the past fifty years, we have seen models of grief evolve and adapt through severance, detachment, stages, tasks, linear processes and oscillating processes to continuation and ongoing attachment. What will the future reveal?

From the medical model, bereavement counselling is borrowing the principle of evidence-based practice, basing more recent theories on what the bereaved find supportive. This must surely be an improvement upon former models, which tended to pathologise grief that did not conform to the ordained pattern or the latest guru's schema. Even though I have my own pictorial metaphor for the journey of grief, I am not convinced that one can ever set a template in place. Those of us who support, or write about, the bereaved can never dictate—we can only observe. Increasingly, it is the voice of the bereaved themselves that is heard within our approaches, and my own contribution to the field is outlined here and in more detail in the Stepping Stones programme for bereaved parents, explored in *Section II*.

Observing the expedition that bereaved parents were undertaking, I realised that the continuing attachment to their deceased child would undoubtedly impact on the rest of their life. Parents often said, 'you never get over it, you just get used to it,' implicitly expressing the interweaving of their deceased child's life—and death—with the rest of their family story. The following representation evolved out of the understanding that change is an inevitable part of life; all living things change, it is a definition of life. Most changes, however, carry elements of loss—some barely significant and some bringing devastating anguish. The tragic losses will result in grief, but those who grieve will also discover new things, even if it is only the hitherto unimagined depths of the pain of loss. With new discoveries there are elements of growth, and when an organism grows, it changes. Thus the cycle is complete, only to be repeated again and again throughout life, for we cannot experience changes without some losses, and, as long as we live, we are compelled to change.

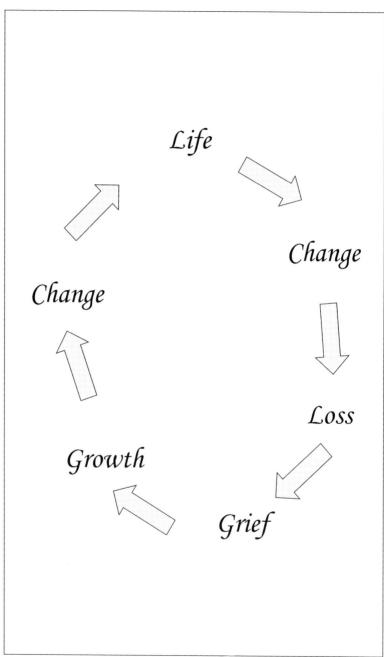

Lifecircle (Shirley Potts, 1997)

It is a model that is neither linear nor oscillating, although it bears more resemblance to the latter than the former, but circular and repetitive. Indeed, the very term model denigrates the experience, which is far more fluid and accommodating than a structured process would imply. It is more of a concept. I would not presume to set guidelines for grieving, or a progressive pattern. Rather, I observed the course of my client group and recorded their structure of meaning as they wrestled with the most challenging experience of their lives. Few of them had read Freud or Bowlby, or heard of Worden, Walter, Stroebe or Klass. They rarely spoke the language of the textbooks. I recall one bereaved—and exasperated—mother once snapping at me: 'Don't call it bereavement. I just miss him.'

Nevertheless, much of the language of the 'talking therapies' is slipping into common usage and it is satisfying to see a society that is beginning to reject the antiquated maxim of 'least said, soonest mended', and learning instead that the sharing of personal and professional narratives is a valuable tool in our evolving understanding of grief and mourning.

If learning to live with death is the essential endeavour of the bereaved, then learning to live alongside those undertaking that endeavour is the role allocated to those of us who choose to accompany, sustain and support them. There is no definitive model or process. The words of a bereaved mother state this eloquently:

'It must have been a psychologist who invented the clinically slick term of "the grieving process".

What a ludicrously inappropriate phrase to define the mental, physical and emotional turmoil that you are left to sort out after your child has died. I can think of no other trauma in life which is so crudely and ineptly called a process...

The "grieving process" conveys nothing other than a mechanical method of accounting for certain stages in grief. It implies that it is a continual going forward in an orderly progressive way. Nothing could be less true.

Grieving takes no account of an orderly disciplined progress. It is erratic and chooses its own winding path which may make as many diversions, detours and circuits as it needs.

*Why do we allow our deepest feelings to be sterilised by a
meaningless label like "the grieving process"?
Why don't we stop trying to compartmentalise grief and
call it what it really is—learning to live with death.'*
(Shawe, 1992)

I have had opportunity to observe how it is for families bereaved
of a child—grief; learning to live with death—and I have been offered some insight into their journey. For most bereaved families,
life after the loss of their child is uncharted territory; a journey of
unknown destination for which the maps of previous expeditions
can offer only guidance or caution, but no precise route to follow.

References

Aries P (1981) *The Hour of our Death.* Allen Lane, London

Bowlby J (1969) *Attachment and Loss.* Basic Books, New York

Clark D, Seymour J (2002) *Reflections on Palliative Care.* Open University Press, Buckingham

Engel GL (1961)Is grief a disease? *Psychosom Med* **23**: 18–22

Freud S (1917) *The Complete Works of Sigmund Freud.* Hogarth Press,
New York

Freud S (1910) *Five Lectures on Psycho-Analysis.* Hogarth, London

Gorer G (1965) *Death, Grief and Mourning in Contemporary Britain.*
The Cresset Press, London

Harmon We (1992) *The Top 500 Poems.* Columbia University Press,
New York

Jupp P, Gittings C (1999) *Death in England.* Manchester University
Press, Manchester

Klass D, Silverman P, Nickman S (1996) *Continuing Bonds.* Taylor
and Francis, Philadelphia

Kubler-Ross E (1970) *On Death and Dying.* Routledge, London

Kuykendall J (1998) (Ed, Potts, S.) London, pp. Masterclass

Levinas E (2000) *God, Death and Time.* Stanford University Press,
Stanford, CA

McCracken A, Semel M (1998) *A Broken Heart Still Beats*. Hazelden, Minnesota

Nelson-Jones R (1995) *The Theory and Practice of Counselling*. Cassell, London

Obershaw RJ (1999) In: Children and Death 4th International Conference, Bristol, UK

Parkes CM (1972) *Bereavement: Studies in Adult Life*. Sage, London

Raphael B, Middleton W, Martinek N, Miso V (1993)Counselling and therapy of the bereaved. In: Stroebe M, Stroebe W, Hansson RO, eds. *Handbook of Bereavement*. Cambridge University Press, Cambridge

Rosenblatt PC (2000a) *Parent Grief: Narratives of Loss and Relationship*. Brunner/Mazel, Philadelphia

Rosenblatt PC (2000b) Parents talking in the present tense about their dead child. *Bereavement Care* **19**: 35–38

Shawe ME (1992) *Enduring, Sharing, Loving*. Dartman, Longman, Todd, London

Sheldon F (1997) *Psychosocial Palliative Care*. Stanley Thornes, Cheltenham

Simpson M (1979) *Dying, Death and Grief: A Critical Bibliography*. University of Philadelphia Press, Philadelphia

Stroebe M (1992)Coping with bereavement: A review of the griefwork hypothesis. *Omega* **26**: 19–42

Stroebe M, Gergen M, Gergen K, Stroebe W (1992) Broken hearts or broken bonds. *Am Psycholog* **47**: 1205–12

Stroebe M, Schut H (1998) Culture and grief. *Bereavement Care* **17**: 7–11

Stroebe M, Schut H (1995)The Dual Process model of coping with loss. In: *International Workgroup on Death, Dying and Bereavement*, Oxford, UK

Stroebe M, Stroebe W, Hansson RO (1993) *Handbook of Bereavement: Theory, Research and Intervention*. Cambridge University Press, Cambridge

Walter T (1999) *On Bereavement: The Culture of Grief*. Open University Press, Buckingham

Walter T (1994) *The Revival of Death*. Routledge, London

Walter T (1991) Modern death—taboo or not taboo? *Sociology* **25**: 293–310

Worden JW (1996) *Children and Grief.* Guildford Press, New York

Worden JW (1991) *Grief Counselling and Grief Therapy*, 2nd edn. Routledge, London

Worden JW (1988) *Grief Counselling and Grief Therapy.* Routledge, London

Wortman CB, Silver RC, Kessler RC (1999) The meaning of loss and adjustment to bereavement. In: Stroebe M, Stroebe W, Hansson RO, eds. *Handbook of Bereavement.* Cambridge University Press, Cambridge

Wortman S, Silver RC (1989) The myths of coping with loss. *J Consult Clinical Psychology* **57**: 349–57.

2

Counselling approaches

Within the realm of bereavement, an increasing variety of support interventions have evolved, to include voluntary organisations, NHS services, telephone helplines, self-help groups, pastoral visitors, internet services, school-based services and more. These do not all necessarily belong beneath the banner of 'counselling' and there are, indeed, groups that honestly style themselves as 'befrienders'. Bereavement is a situation that particularly lends itself to befriending support; for that is undoubtedly what many bereaved people most require—a kind, empathic, listening ear, prepared to sympathetically endure the repetition and reminiscing that is a fundamental part of the grief journey. Many of the interactions I had with families at the hospice did not merit the designation of a counselling relationship and it would be pretentious to assume otherwise. They were supportive, understanding and empathic befriending encounters, with a therapeutic value even so. There are occasions in bereavement where more practised skills are required and the structured approach of a formal counselling schedule is more beneficial.

For those who wish to pursue counselling training, there is a plethora of resources and facilities now available—a visit to the British Association of Counselling and Psychotherapy (BACP) website is a reasonable first step to ascertain the credibility of courses. Beware those who offer a diploma in a weekend; counselling and psychotherapy training should, of necessity, extend across a reasonable period of time. Given the extensive literature now available, I offer a brief and personal overview here of counselling theories I have found most appropriate in bereavement support.

Over the past thirty years a profusion of counselling and psychotherapy approaches has evolved that must baffle the uninitiated. There is yet to be established an informed and mutual agreement between use of the term ' counselling' or

]psychotherapypsychotherapy to describe the activities of those in the 'talking therapy' arenas. However many debates and discussions I peruse on the topic, I return each time to the conviction that the argument is largely semantic, possibly originating from an awareness that 'counselling' was acquiring a somewhat unflattering, and largely feminine, public persona of scarves, candles, gentle empathic nods and encouraging interjections. 'Psychotherapy', on the other hand, could carry much more scientific weight, sounded more highly qualified, and could apply to any gender (not unlike the historical gender and skill weighting of 'doctor' and 'nurse'). It is a personal observation and probably an over-simplistic view of a much more complex situation. However, I do find the debate tiresome when there is already so much to confuse tentative clients who stand on the threshold of therapeutic support. I shall therefore use both terms interchangeably.

Is there a particular title or philosophical model convincingly appropriate for all presenting problems? I think not. There are, no doubt, still those counselling (or psychotherapy) practitioners who peddle their wares, their particular counselling guru, or their specific technique with the evangelistic fervour of one who is convinced they have found the elixir of eternal therapy. I suspect that such partisan rigidity diminishes the acceptability of this approach in a post-modern era of choice and flexibility where truth has become subjective and responses to counselling therapy can vary significantly from client to client. The last two decades have consummated the evolution of integrative methodology and practitioners have become less precious and evangelical about the merits of a particular purist stance. This is not to imply a dilution of original theories, but rather an understanding of overlap and interplay between approaches that can be harnessed and utilised to the benefit of the client. I intend to draw principally from three particular strands that weave into considerations of bereavement counselling. Such a combination of approaches is not unusual within bereavement counselling, as exampled by Machin and Spall who acknowledge a collective person-centred, narrative and cognitive approach in therapeutic encounters with bereaved clients (Machin and Spall, 2004).

Initially trained in a person-centred approach, this remains as the essence of my way of being and I value the original principles on which Carl Rogers founded his theory. However, within the area of bereavement counselling, it is wise to maintain an open mind to several different counselling styles. Death and bereavement are the ubiquitous experiences of society and therefore no particular 'type' of client can be anticipated. Notwithstanding the integrative movements of recent years, it is unlikely that one particular counselling approach will ever be appropriate for all bereaved clients. Parkes makes the valid point that self-referral is the customary route into counselling; yet, in bereavement, there may be those who are desolately lacking in motivation or hope and therefore unlikely to seek out the help they need (Parkes, 2000). In these situations it could be that those working in palliative care are best placed to assess and advise, and at least enlighten the bereaved person regarding support that may be available to them. Immediately this is at variance with non-directive counselling theories, illustrating that bereavement support should not be constrained by an inflexible, uniform approach.

The triad of counselling approaches that I consider most suited to bereavement support work are:

- Person-centred, with its core belief in self-actualisation and the client's inherent ability to comprehend their own process

- Psychodynamic, with its emphasis on the impact of past experiences upon current responses

- Cognitive Behavioural Therapy (CBT), with its effective transformational potential through adapted patterns of thinking.

Each offers the feasibility of a therapeutic encounter and each has a particular light to play on the situation of bereavement, but the common denominator between these and many other counselling approaches is the value of relationship. The counselling relationship brings to bereavement support an environment where a 'professional listener' is prepared to hear their client long after the supplies of empathy, understanding and patience in other listeners have been exhausted. The formal acquisition of psychotherapeutic skills is insufficient to guarantee a therapeutic encounter.

A profound understanding of self and the experiential awareness of one's own journey towards self-actualisation is a required commodity in a counsellor of integrity.

Person-centred

Carl Rogers, who initiated the person-centred counselling approach, spoke of a 'way of being' not only in the counselling relationship but also as a person of integrity beyond the counselling room. Rogers' approach was based on the actualising tendency he saw manifest in the universe. He perceived an inherent tendency in organisms towards maintaining, enhancing and reproducing themselves (Nelson-Jones, 1995). However, early grief is almost an antithesis of that theory—grieving parents, particularly, may be caught in a cycle of disabling, damaging and destroying themselves. If there is an innate drive towards self-actualisation, it is severely incapacitated by grief. Nevertheless, there are elements of a person-centred approach that are indispensable to bereavement counselling and support. Rogers understood the potency of the relationship and stressed the core values that were essential components at the heart of a functional counsellor's character and relationships with clients: empathy, congruence and unconditional positive regard—sometimes translated as warmth, honesty and acceptance (Rogers, 1961). Whichever phraseology is used, the three conditions constitute a philosophy and a personality that most clients would be comfortable being close to.

Empathy

This is a valuable skill much abused within bereavement support. Just as many people consider themselves to be 'good listeners', so most people feel they can empathise when necessary. It is widely imagined that the empathic response is: 'I know how you feel', or 'I'm with you in this', or 'I'm here if you need me'. Kindly and sympathetic supporters and friends feel they are offering true empathic understanding to the bereaved as they refer to similar situations in their own lives. 'I was just like you are when my mother died...'

Actually, 'I know how you feel' is never an appropriate empathic response, even when said by one bereaved parent to another. There is certainly an understanding and fellowship there that is absent in many other encounters, but no one knows how another person feels. We can begin to imagine, perhaps, and some imaginations may be better equipped with similar experiences than others, but we can never make assumptions. Empathy has been colloquialised as 'walking a mile in the other one's moccasins' and were we to truly inhabit the phenomenological viewpoint of our client, we would probably appreciate the futility of imagining we can 'know' how they feel. Nevertheless, those who seek support do value the sincere endeavours of the counsellor who determines to perceive the uniqueness of their client's situation.

Practising the skill of empathy requires concentration, perseverance and honest self-reflection, all encased within a sincerity which assures a client that concern is genuine and not simply a cerebral exercise. It is quite likely, within a counselling career, that therapists will encounter those whose responses to conflict, difficulty or trauma may bear no resemblance to responses the counsellor might have made. The keystone of empathy is to remain fixed upon the circumstances and viewpoint of the client.

A deeper level of empathy can only operate within a relationship of trust, and this is not likely to be instantaneous. The area of counsellor self-disclosure continues to provoke debate and is relevant to the establishment of a trusting relationship. While excessive or inappropriate disclosure of personal detail by the counsellor may contaminate professionalism, Audet observes client feedback revealed that the greatest impact on the counselling process had emanated from the counsellor's measured but fairly intimate self-disclosure (Audet and Everall, 2003). It has been suggested that counsellors intend disclosure to increase similarity and empathy between themselves and clients (Edwards and Murdock, 1994). Within bereavement counselling, this introduces once more the discourse between supporters who are themselves bereaved and those who have not closely experienced bereavement. My own response to this polemic is that counselling skills and sensitivity of approach should and must take precedence over the prior experiences of the counsellor. Personal experience of bereavement by the counsellor is equally liable to mutilate or enhance the therapeutic encounter and I suspect the risk of harm outweighs the benefit of commonality. Those who enter counselling training with a personal history of trauma—be it bereavement, abuse or any other personal suffering—have an ethical responsibility to ensure their own issues are thoroughly expurgated and resolved before useful self-disclosure within the counselling situation can be entertained.

Once trust and confidence are sufficiently established, the counsellor may notice opportunities to identify a hidden agenda, where there is, perhaps, a discrepancy between a client's speech and their body language or manner. In these circumstances a counsellor may be able to gently observe the discrepancies, bringing them sensitively to the client's awareness in order that the unacknowledged feelings might be more clearly understood. Empathy is naturally enhanced by active listening skills, a mainstay of many basic-level counselling courses and, indeed, bereavement counselling or befriending courses. My own interest in counselling was evoked many years ago by a 'listening weekend' where participants could encounter and experiment with some of the basic skills inherent in pastoral support of others. My horrified discovery that I found it almost impossible to *listen* to someone for five minutes, responding only with facial expression, sent me scurrying off to train more thoroughly in counselling skills! Listening meticulously, competently, considerately and helpfully requires practice, as does the ability to sit comfortably with silence when necessary. I look back and cringe at my earliest efforts to fill every silence with platitudes or 'rescuing' remarks. Rescuing indicates an intolerance of the angst of our client and a compulsion to change the subject, trivialise, or draw conclusions on their behalf. It is an omnipresent danger within bereavement support, most often seen in those who interact with bereaved children, but also features in adult exchanges too—those banalities often overheard at funerals: 'at least the sun's shining, it's always harder in the rain isn't it?' 'Well, the worst is over now, isn't it?' 'Your garden is looking lovely...'

Ah well, our heritage is deeply embedded.

Congruence

This is a characteristic that I have colloquialised as being the same on the outside as the inside. The antithesis to hypocrisy, I suppose, and yet some levels of 'hypocrisy' are acceptable forms of polite behaviour so it is impossible to be too dogmatic in its criticism. Congruence is often a natural characteristic of early childhood that sublimates itself to the adaptive processes of maturity. How often have we heard parents relate with amused embarrassment tales of outspoken curiosity in their progeny, or the inevitable candid remark of the three-year-old who has no compunction about commenting on someone's appearance? After extricating ourselves uncomfortably from the awkwardness of the enquiry to the stranger on the bus—'Why are your teeth yellow?'—we await our children's evolution into polite, reserved, incongruent adults. For adults, the polite enquiry after another's health or well-being does not generally anticipate or precipitate a detailed account of medical analysis when a simple 'fine, thank you' is all that is actually expected. However, within the counselling context, congruence is a specific and essential tool. It relates closely to the integrity and transparency of the counsellor: 'The counsellor should be herself in the relationship, putting up no professional front or personal facade' (Rogers, 1978).

Unnecessary distraction occurs when a counsellor is struggling to maintain a serene, listening exterior while grappling internally to construct the 'right' response, or maintain their considered professional equilibrium. Congruence, then, is a quality that requires internal ratification as well as external manifestation. Immediacy—that skill of being 'in the moment' with the client—can also be lost when the counsellor is preoccupied, ransacking their mind for the appropriate, professional, or impressive response instead of giving full attendance to their client. Consider, for example, the scenario in bereavement counselling where a mother is recounting her thoughts as she visits her child's grave; the wistful regrets of unspoken futures, and the painful recrimination that persistently maintains mothers should always be able to 'make it better' for their children... How many times have some counsellors endured such sessions through gritted teeth, exhorting themselves silently but forcefully not to cry? Other counsellors, myself included, might accept philosophically the welling of tears as a normal response to such moving encounters, and be able to focus on the client's material. Clearly, the counsellor should not become so overwhelmed with distress as to prompt rescue from the client. There is a marked difference between silent tears and racking sobs, and the counsellor whose distress is unmanageable would be well advised to seek immediate supervision and consider seriously their ability to beneficially support in such situations. In working with bereaved families, I was constantly reminded that the grief of others will make me sad, yet I must accept that it is *their* grief and *my* sadness (Rochford, 1991). To be sad with them is both empathic and congruent—to be grief-stricken with them would be excessive and unhelpful. The debate continues regarding the valuable or detrimental effects of shedding tears when with a client and it remains open to individual assessment, preference and personality. I would simply add that in relation to congruence, it is difficult to maintain transparency with a client while endeavouring to conceal internal machinations. Mearns gives the reassurance that 'the development of congruence requires the trainee counsellor to forsake the tendency to portray acceptable ways of being and risk being themselves.' (Mearns, 1994). Decades ago, Kopp confessed to a challenging depth of congruence when he wrote, 'As a psychotherapist, I am no longer willing to accept anyone as my patient to whose pain I do not feel vulnerable… If I am not able to be open to their pain, I may perhaps find professional satisfaction in working with them, but no personal joy' (Kopp, 1972).

The association between empathy and congruence is obvious, with the common denominator being honest self-awareness. That is not to say that the empathic response is necessarily congruent, or vice versa, but empathy that was expressed but not echoed internally by the counsellor would be a hollow and shabby thing. Wosket describes how empathic responses have their limitations when the experience a client describes is far beyond the imaginative capabilities of the counsellor striving for empathy. In these situations, the congruent response from the counsellor—'I cannot imagine what you feel'—could effectively deepen trust and acceptance (Wosket, 1999). Congruence must always be balanced with compassion and understanding; it is never the intention to brutalise with honesty or carelessly dismantle a client's self-constructed protective scaffolding with excruciatingly painful haste. The balance is crucial, for although many of the characteristics associated with congruence carry wholesome attributes, like honesty, genuineness, transparency, there are still associated anxieties. With transparency, is there not a fear of inadvertent or unwanted exposure? With honesty, is there not an associated fear of insensitive wounding? Congruence is not to be confused with forthright remarks or blunt accusation. Even Rogers acknowledged that congruence does not mean that counsellors, '...blurt out impulsively every passing feeling' (Rogers, 1961).

Congruence, explicitly practised, also incorporates a modelling process whereby clients are encouraged to be real in the relationship. With what Nelson-Jones describes as 'a mutuality of congruence', clients are enabled and empowered to become more congruent, even in their relationships outside the counselling room (Nelson-Jones, 1999). This ripple effect is one of the most positive manifestations of congruence, as honesty and genuineness begin to pervade all aspects of a person's life. In this respect, congruence can often be seen as a foundation for assertiveness training. The client who is enabled to voice their inner feelings and be heard without condemnation will also be empowered to state wishes, requests, or feelings in other environments with growing confidence. An example from my own experience with bereaved parents might be the response given to the ubiquitous enquiry as to how many children they have. This question seems to arise in manifold social situations and bereaved parents are often confounded by it. To include a deceased child in the number might require further explanation or create confusion—and likely discomfort on the part of the enquirer. However, to exclude the child from the figure seems to be an incongruent response on the part of the bereaved parent, leading to subsequent guilty feelings of betrayal. The client who has become more real, or at ease with their fluctuating emotion is more able to say, 'I have three children, but one has died.' Explanation may or may not follow, but parents feel they have been true to themselves and have less residual discomfort in hearing their own statements.

Supervision is possibly the environment where congruence is able to radiate and inform most visibly. The relationship between supervisor and supervisee is different to that of client/therapist, although with many, if not all, similar skills exercised. I suspect there is not the same degree of reticence (on the part of a supervisor) to verbalise congruent feelings, as there may be on the part of therapist-with-client. While a client may be slowly unpacking their thoughts and discovering their inner self, the supervisee-with-supervisor is presumed to have attained appropriate levels of self-awareness and the inner strength and confidence to tolerate honest self-examination. Indeed, the primary purpose of supervision is for such a process of reflexivity in the presence of an experienced and congruent practitioner who can elucidate internalised reactions and responses in the supervisee to encourage and facilitate the expression of congruence in future practice.

It is important not to confuse congruence with a simple revelation of the inner thoughts of the counsellor. Working with bereaved parents, I frequently worked with couples, perhaps seeing each of them individually. Confidentiality and safe boundaries demanded that I do *not* reveal issues from one partner to another. Was I being incongruent? In those specific situations it is for the counsellor to evaluate the honesty of the encounter within an environment of confidence and trust. I once talked with a profoundly saddened and weary mother as we sat at the bedside of her dying son. I was listening to the mother's anxieties about her son's feelings and her own responses, but I was tired and felt my eyes drawn to the young man in the bed, literally breathing his final few hours. As I gazed at him, I thought of other youngsters and feelings they had expressed in the face of approaching death. Then I heard his mother say, 'I'm rambling, aren't I?' and I realised she knew I had stopped hearing her fully. I apologised and admitted I was watching her son's breathing. While I am sure she understood, with no recrimination, I felt I had allowed my mind to wander when I could have more congruently addressed the issues that she and her son were raising in me.

It is a counselling skill of great worth—a counsellor lacking in sincerity, integrity or honesty would be a pale shadow of their intended persona. The root of the word 'sincere' comes from *sans cerre* meaning 'without wax'. The linguistics evolved from the ancient Greek practice of pouring wax over marble statues or busts to conceal any cracks and flaws in the marble, thus deceiving prospective purchasers. A *sans cerre* piece of work then, without wax, was much to be prized, as indeed is the quality the word has come to represent. It is unsurprising that the practice of congruence should feature in Rogers' core conditions of the therapeutic relationship; it may even be the primary condition that undergirds so many other interactions. 'I am convinced that it is in the area of therapist congruence that the greatest advances can and should be made' (Thorne, 1996).

Unconditional positive regard

This describes Rogers' renowned commitment to 'prizing' the other person; acknowledging their right to exist, even when their viewpoint, life-choices, responses or character may bear no resemblance whatsoever to your own. Rogers' terminology may seem rather clumsy now—and current authors and practitioners may be more likely to speak of being non-judgemental. In an age where non-discriminatory practice is given much greater credence and is sustained by legislation, it is easy to assume that unconditional positive regard is an automatic conclusion. Rogers' rather verbose description of the skill should nevertheless be examined for it includes qualities that transcend mere endeavours to 'not judge'. When he spoke of *prizing* an individual, it incorporated a warmth and genuine interest in the other that is not necessarily attained in all relationships even when no discrimination or judgement exists. Consider your own experiences—do you have a sense of when someone simply does not *like* you? Invisible barriers appear, a discomforting feeling creeps into the conversation, and you may cautiously consider your every utterance for fear of exacerbating the disapproval you already sense. This may not be a discriminatory or judgemental issue, but it has powerful connotations nonetheless. Naturally, there are those situations in life where two people simply cannot relate, would not choose to be friends and can continue their existence blithely ignorant of the other. The counselling situation must rise above such details. Now the intertwining of the three core conditions becomes even more complex. How can the counsellor empathise with someone she cannot relate to? And if she attempts to proceed on a professional level with inner reservations, what has become of congruence?

This is one of the reasons that worthwhile counselling training is extensive in time and profound in self-examination. Most accredited courses in counselling and psychotherapy training will require a period of personal therapy for the trainee. Critics have dismissed such introspection as puerile navel-gazing, but the degree of a counsellor's self-awareness will directly impact upon their ability to offer unconditional positive regard. A familiar edict within counselling is the reminder that an individual cannot always affect the actions and character of those around them, but each individual *can* be responsible for their own reactions and responses. It is in this area that the experienced counsellor has learned to value and respect a client, regardless of what situation or character trait has brought them to the counselling room. Each word of Rogers' phrase carries immeasurable weight.

Unconditional: without conditions, a state of allowing every client their individuality without indemnity clauses or provisos. A counsellor should have sufficiently unpacked their own emotional baggage to know why, where, and when any internalised responses exist, and have the inner resources to sublimate them;

Positive: an affirmative response is required. This is not to imply a rose-tinted optimistic view of the client or situation, but to be assured that the therapeutic encounter will be beneficial, progress will be made, a relationship will be established;

Regard: this is the valuing, prizing, respecting element of the skill. The conviction that every other soul on the planet has as much right to be here as you do. It is a way of being that reflects the warmth, honesty and acceptance that summarise Rogers' original core conditions.

Psychodynamic

The psychodynamic counselling approach, as its name suggests, finds its roots in Freudian psychoanalysis. Although some Freudian theories are considered to be outdated, they brought much insight and understanding to the embryonic profession of counselling and have had an influence on current theories and practice. Freud, Jung, Klein and Erikson have each given their name to particular strands of psychodynamic theory, thus one might hear of a Jungian or Kleinian therapist. This can cause some confusion for the uninitiated as the practice of psychodynamic counselling bears very little resemblance to Freud's original concept of psychoanalysis (Jacobs, 2002). *Psychoanalysis* generally implies therapy that is likely to continue over an extended period of time with sessions two or three times a week. *Psychodynamic* owes its title to the concept of the mind/emotions/feelings (psyche) being active and interactive (dynamic) not only in relation to other people, but also in relation to itself. Despite the fabled associations with insanity, it is true that we all talk to ourselves, and what we say to ourselves can often have its roots in childhood and early experiences. The psychodynamic counsellor is trained in personal development and has an understanding of theories of personality.

Many of today's psychodynamically trained practitioners would style themselves as *integrative*, just as many practitioners trained within another school of thought might incorporate a psychodynamic approach into their own integrative practice. As already mentioned, the rigid lines between various counselling philosophies have blurred in recent years. This does not have to indicate a dilution from the original concentrate, but more a refinement of successful therapeutic techniques and approaches. The last three decades have heralded a period of consolidation where therapists have been increasingly willing to be informed by other models of practice and the evaluation of successful outcomes for clients. Fiedler noted some time ago that the more mature a therapist becomes, the more similarity in approach they share with mature colleagues from different theoretical modalities. Indeed, the mature therapists were closer to older 'others' than to younger therapists from their own school of thought

(Fiedler, 1950). Does this imply increasing tolerance or increasing wisdom as we age?

One of the most distinctive features of psychodynamic theory is the counsellor's knowledge and use of 'the transference'. Transference and counter-transference refer to the inclination for client—and sometimes counsellor—to repeat in the counselling session, ways in which they relate to significant people in other areas of their life. Often these may be patterns that were set in childhood; the counsellor may be subconsciously viewed as an authority-figure, or a parent-figure, be that nurturing or critical. In counter-transference, it is as if the counsellor responds in character, complying with the role into which the client has thrust them. Unless recognised and acknowledged in order to be utilised as a therapeutic tool, counter-transference can simply become collusion, and that may leave both parties temporarily but artificially satiated, with no real psychotherapy in progress, but rather a distinct possibility of negative and destructive consequences. Much more extensive and informative discussions on transference and psychodynamic theory are available, some of which can be found in the bibliography. For now, we return to the area of bereavement to study the perspectives that psychodynamic theory can bring to approaches with bereaved parents.

Psychodynamic approaches will collect much more detailed data for the purpose of assessment and continuing therapy. A family tree may be drawn, for example, and past problems, in addition to the presenting problem, may be considered. Loss history can be a relevant and useful discussion topic in the arena of bereavement. The death of someone close is probably the worst, but may not be the only, kind of loss a person can experience. In some circumstances I would complete a time-line with a client, recording all their recollections, from childhood to present, of major events in their life. This might include school changes, death of a grandparent, arrival of a sibling, going to college, getting married and so on. All of these events will carry an element of change and many will hold associative feelings of loss. Clients are encouraged to consider how they have responded and acclimatised to loss in the past. While the death of a child will be the worst event on their time-line, bereaved parents can reassure themselves that they do possess some, albeit limited, survival techniques.

They are not entirely inexperienced in the realm of loss. Some clients, of course, may have a more depressing history of loss than others, having perhaps encountered earlier bereavements, divorce, career failure, redundancy, hysterectomy... These accumulated losses may make someone particularly vulnerable to additional and major losses.

In the psychodynamic tradition, reactions to loss will be grounded in childhood experiences and many bereaved people will have taken their response cue from their own parents. What were the 'house rules'? Be strong? Or take to your bed? Talk about your feelings? Or maintain a dignified silence? Utilise friendships? Or value privacy? As a child, it is impossible to discern right and wrong in these attitudes and conventions and, as an adult, I would be reluctant to arbitrate between supposedly acceptable and unacceptable constructs of family life. Whatever background or circumstances a client has experienced, the knowledge and awareness of it, and the ability to reflect upon that understanding is the instrumental factor in counselling. Self-awareness again features highly as an empowering factor for bereaved clients who are struggling to comprehend their turbulent emotions.

Although I have interwoven the three approaches of person-centred, psychodynamic and cognitive-behavioural, there are elements of quite radical divergence that must be acknowledged. For example, while Rogers' core conditions are a foundational tenet to many counselling approaches—and, as counsellor qualities, are always to be desired—the offering of warmth and positive regard to clients must be viewed, in the psychodynamic tradition, from the perspective of negative transference. The counsellor who consciously or subconsciously embodies a 'nurturing parent' role, runs the risk of also 'failing' as a parent and repeating anticipated disappointments for the client. This can produce the fertile terrain for fruitful psychodynamic therapy, as the experience of having or being a 'failed' parent is far more common than its antithesis and many clients find their healing is facilitated when they finally abandon the futile hope of changing their past rather than their future. The skilled psychodynamic practitioner will work with transference and counter-transference in a very productive and beneficial way. The integrative practitioner who may be sampling a psychodynamic approach to assess its merit within bereavement work, should at least understand that the context to the counselling is a pivotal issue. Not only will this include a client's prior experiences, but also their current circumstances and support structures. One of the aspects counsellors overlook, at times, is the understanding that what takes place in the counselling session is a mere fraction of that client's time and may not necessarily be the greatest influence to which they are exposed. McLeod and Machin suggested that the 'narrow slice of time' of the counselling session is to be contrasted with a social framework that exists before and after the counselling session (McLeod and Machin, 1998). This is nowhere more relevant than within the area of bereavement counselling. The client must be perceived within the context of their social world, as therapy will be heavily influenced by those around the client, many of whom may be diametrically opposed to the style of support espoused within the 'narrow slice of time' of the counselling session. All too often, I have been an impotent observer of the conflict a client must endure when the counselling support is at variance with the 'house-rules'. I know bereaved clients have had to tolerate comments like, 'What do you mean, "the counsellor said it's alright to cry over the photo-albums"?—You're just making yourself worse; put them away and do something else.' I can only admire the courage of those clients who have pitted their inner convictions against a deeply embedded social construct, with only a modicum of support from counselling.

In psychodynamic counselling, endings are important and will be planned for well in advance. Endings are, of course, significant to most counselling approaches, but the psychodynamic counsellor would be particularly aware of the disappointment, relief, sadness or other feelings that may surface at times of separation. It was the influence of psychodynamic theory that decreed the length and conclusions of the *Stepping Stones programme* instituted for bereaved parents at Derian House. Parents are aware of the ending from the beginning and the final sessions focus specifically on the conclusions and accompanying reactions and feelings.

In conclusion—some thoughts about the narrative process. This has evolved comparatively recently (Angus *et al*, 1999;

McLeod, 1997; Meier, 2002) as a psychotherapy model and practitioners and researchers are producing some fascinating material on the topic (Klass, 1999; Meier, 2002; Rosenblatt, 2000). There are, however, some observations specific to bereavement counselling that indicate a variance with some of the assumptions of narratologists. Meier, citing Crites, suggests that 'the momentary present embraces one's whole experience, the past remembered as fixed and the future that is fluid, awaiting determination, subject to alternative scenarios' (Meier, 2002). My experience with bereaved families would suggest remembrance of the past, as portrayed in client narrative, is far from fixed—and this mutability may in itself constitute the core of the therapeutic process. It is the journey towards a conceptual, if somewhat resigned, acceptance of the past that facilitates a client's process through the psychotherapeutic encounter towards re-establishing wholeness in a previously fragmented psyche. The abundance of emanating material on narrative approaches provides opportunity to examine the minutiae of a process that has existed as long as language itself. We may now at least offer scientific, epistemological scaffolding to the anecdotal evidence of centuries that assured us of the value of telling stories, and how these stories might be adapted and amended under times of stress, or while the narrator is establishing for themselves the conclusive, acceptable and tolerable version.

Cognitive Behavioural Therapy

Aaron Beck, the originator of cognitive therapy, made the astute observation that the ways in which people think of themselves will have a significant impact upon the development of, and responses to, emotional and behavioural difficulties (Beck, 1976). Much is promulgated regarding the efficacy of positive self-talk and, with the advent of life-coaching and other such mentoring and motivating roles, the determined, triumphant language of optimism is rife in our time. However, some negative embedded precepts from childhood and influential figures in a client's life tend to be rather more persistent than a simple vocabulary change could rectify. Inner thoughts and self-talk certainly have a major function in emotional equilibrium and it is the adaptation of these, over time, that cognitive behavioural therapy is largely concerned with. The most internalised of our inner voices will be the most difficult to change, as it is this innermost dialogue that tells the true story of a person's self-regard. The person with arachnophobia may be perfectly capable of rationalising their own size and ability compared to a spider, but the deeply embedded fear may only dissipate through experience, repetition, evidence and assurance.

In bereavement counselling, cognitive therapies (Ellis, 1989) have a role in offering both permission and edification to a client. Knowledge is power, and some understanding of grief processes and 'normal' adaptive responses to a traumatic event can sustain grievers in tolerating their vulnerable state. Equally, this enlarged understanding can be helpful in giving the grieving client 'permission' to be as they are. Cognitive approaches can encourage and assist clients in the revision of their thinking, where that thinking is unhelpful in grief (Neimeyer and Anderson, 2002).

Missing information can cause painful self-recrimination in the bereaved client who has never been informed of the possible physical symptoms of grief. Many a client has been visibly and gratefully relieved when informed, through bereavement counselling, that the symptoms they thought indicated neurosis or madness were, in fact, 'normal' reactions to the trauma of bereavement—a normal reaction to an abnormal situation (Herbert, 1996). The difficulty for practitioners in this area is that working with cognitive processes and shared knowledge bases can bring the encounter into close proximity with the danger of social power issues. Engaging with these issues will need to be cautiously and sensitively addressed—the 'child-likeness of grief' has been addressed in the *Stepping Stones* section of this book—but, with all respect to the maturity of grievers, it is particularly the case in bereavement counselling that the client sometimes feels small and exposed, while the practitioner carries 'knowledge and expertise'.

The task of the cognitive therapist is to examine, jointly with the client, those deeply embedded 'rules for living' that a client may carry, and assess the helpfulness, relevance, and effectiveness of those rules to the current situation. Injunctions such as 'big boys don't cry', 'be strong in front of the children', or 'let it all hang out', may have evolved into idioms that are now regarded with some scepticism, but their power to influence will take generations to attenuate. Such and similar edicts create a family vocabulary that is unconsciously but powerfully absorbed by family members, and continues to influence throughout life. Much of this influence is consistent with the natural generational progression of families and there are 'rules for living' learned in earliest life that maintain the very structure of individuals, families and society. (To arrive at adulthood with a blank canvas free of any philosophical outlook or moral and social framework for life is not only highly unlikely, but would imply enormous mental and emotional deprivation. The rare examples we have of feral children (Newton, 2002) corroborate this.) However, while many entrenched rules for living continue to offer valid data for daily life, other earlier influences may have become obsolete and irrelevant, may even be considered so, intellectually, by the individual, yet their influence continues to permeate.

Thus, the client who has experienced a devastating bereavement arrives at the counsellor's door with a multitude of preconceptions and cognitive patterns. Many will prove helpful to the griever's current situation and may well be maintaining a sufficient level of social functioning for the bereaved person to survive, at least superficially, from day to day. Other cognitive patterns, however, may be detrimental to a bereaved person's healthy navigation of the journey of grief. Beliefs, in themselves, do not necessarily cause emotional distress, but there is a connection between cognition, emotion and behaviour. It is the cognitive processes that can challenge the other two functions.

The simple analogy is that of a student preoccupied, for example, with writing. They begin to feel *thirsty*. As the feeling reaches consciousness, they *think* they should get a drink of water, so finally they *act* by going to pour a glass of water. This is the *feel, think, act,* or affective, cognitive and behavioural cycle that governs many of our daily actions. Through utilisation of cognitive awareness and process, some feelings and actions might be adjusted; i.e. the student's knowledge of the benefits of hydration to learning might encourage the maintenance of an adequate intake of water to prevent any feelings of thirst disturbing concentration.

This is a poor and simplistic analogy when compared to the overwhelming feelings of grief and responses to those feelings. Nevertheless, some element of a similar procedure is present when the grieving client is enabled to have a cognitive grasp on their experiences. Many bereaved people will pursue literature on grief, writings of other bereaved parents, books about theories of grief, if only to validate or question their personal response to grief.

The cognitive therapist can assist and encourage a client to sift through the detritus of a lifetime's accumulated 'rules' and salvage the worthy while challenging the unhelpful injunctions. It is never as facile as 'wrong' thinking being replaced by 'right' thinking; rather, a collaborative rapport is established between therapist and client whereby alternative interpretations of events and beliefs can be examined within an environment of acceptance and encouragement. Spong and Hollanders, who discuss 'power-sensitised counselling', sympathetically address the power differential of the counselling situation that can so subtly undermine the therapeutic process. Disparities are minimised when the client is supported in discovering their own alternative perspective rather than suffering the imposition of a counsellor's viewpoint (Spong and Hollanders, 2003). These authors also reiterate the parallels between cognitive and narrative therapy:

> '*Both the cognitive therapist and the narrative therapist encourage the client to find their own alternative view or discourse into which they can position themselves and from which they can construct a more empowering story.*'

As part of an integrative approach, both psychodynamic approaches and cognitive therapy methodology tend to suggest themselves when a client is particularly self-critical. Commonly, it is the punitive superego, or the internalised critical parent, exhorting the griever to 'pull yourself together' or 'stop feeling so sorry for yourself'. The language of 'shoulds, oughts and musts' is often indicative of the emotional self-flagellation that grievers are enduring. I have sat many times with a bereaved parent who is insisting that by four months after their child's death, they should surely be crying less, or feeling less distressed. Often the simple reassurance that four months (or five, or six, or seven…) is not a very long period to acclimatise to such a shattering event can bring comfort and relief to a griever.

In scrutinising the affective, cognitive, behavioural process, clients can be empowered and encouraged to pre-empt thorny situations, rather than being coerced by purely affective responses and influences. For example, anniversaries are especially poignant for bereaved families and can arouse overwhelming feelings of dread and foreboding. These feelings can not be negated, but if grievers anticipate and plan for such occasions—perhaps with a memorialisation activity rather than passive avoidance—then the subsequent feelings of control and direction can alleviate some of the pain of being hostage to the calendar.

It is clear that elements of various counselling approaches can blend effectively into a supportive response to bereavement and the above three schools have been utilised to good effect in bereavement support. Various authors have propagated the concept of behavioural counselling becoming more humanistic and it is not difficult to understand how these approaches have intertwined so readily (Lazarus, 1995). I return always to the belief that a perceptive application of Rogers' core conditions should inevitably establish a counselling or helping relationship of value. A warm, honest, accepting relationship is the inimitable ingredient of a therapeutic rapport and will carry immeasurable impact within bereavement support.

The place of assessment

Assessment can carry with it connotations of a diagnostic or judgemental procedure that may diminish the individuality of each client's situation. There should be a compulsion to appreciate the *context* of each loss, as well as a client's receptivity to a particular counselling approach. The distinctiveness of each client is an essential ingredient of bereavement support interventions as parents (and professionals) are tempted to compare degrees of grief. A table of risk factors associated with poor outcome after bereavement has been widely published (Parkes *et al*, 1996), which, while undoubtedly helpful from a scientific and statistical viewpoint for practitioners, cannot avoid carrying with it an inclination to make comparisons. Bereaved families themselves may resort to comparing the loss of a six-month-old baby with a sixteen-year-old adolescent. However, such debate is fraught with danger for families whose emotional resources are too depleted to see beyond their own grief and pain. One of the purposes and opportunities of assessment is to reassure families that their grief is *their* grief and is not being evaluated on a scale of one to ten.

Within the remit of bereavement counselling, certainly at the hospice, there is little scope for implementing selection criteria, as families are essentially pre-selected by virtue of their loss. In this sense, the assessment process utilised owes more to my person-centred roots of perceiving each client's unique frame of reference, their own phenomenological experience of grief and loss, their own locus of evaluation and their own instinctive growth towards full functioning—even where that may mean functioning fully as a griever. My approach to assessment was influenced by Lazarus' multi-modal therapy, or, as he re-phrased it, 'multi-modal assessment followed by appropriate theory' (Dryden, 1991). The convoluted journey of grief necessitates an ongoing assessment, if only informally, as different stages in a client's grief journey may well merit alternative avenues of approach. Lazarus' descriptive phrase of the therapist as an 'authentic chameleon' has always found resonance with me and probably best describes my integrative approach with clients. There is, within that description, a possibility of being perceived as nebulous and ill-defined, but Lazarus' intention was more precise in its objective. It is the honest endeavour to apply validated approaches, pertinent to specific people and circumstances. 'An effective therapist can offer in an authentic manner, different types of relationship to different clients at different times' (Dryden, 1991).

The professional contextual environment in which the counselling is placed may influence assessment. Where grief counselling is enveloped within a multi-professional context, the ideal of a needs-led service may well be compromised by organisational pressures to meet a multiplicity of needs within a constrained period of time (Machin, 1998). Within the hospice environment, there was naturally a proliferation of staff with a medical background, and nursing models tend to be structured, safe and efficient. Obviously, for practitioners with that background, a client-led, non-directive approach can seem tenuous and insecure—although many nurses nobly and competently undertook bereavement support tasks. To offer a guiding framework, I created a Grief Assessment profile, although it was stressed that this was simply a series of reflective *hooks* upon which my colleagues and I could hang our thoughts and considerations. It was not, and was never intended to be, a *pro forma* completed with clients, nor was it a prescriptive or diagnostic implement. It was, however, extremely helpful as a reflective tool to be utilised following visits to families. Practitioners were regularly surprised at the breadth of their knowledge of a client following a visit, a knowledge illuminated and recalled by the topics within the Grief Assessment. The transition from models of care that had a largely medical orientation, into a counselling model, can be a dilemma for both staff and families—and expecting the same professional to undertake both roles is a particularly onerous task. Jim Kuykendall once encapsulated this memorably for me with a reminder that a prescriptive question from the client deserves a prescriptive response. It is not always appropriate to offer the flexible, client-centred response: if a patient asked, 'How often should I take this medicine?' it would not be fitting to respond with, 'How often would you like to take it?' (Kuykendall, 1998).

Thus, the Grief Assessment was conceived in order to offer a link between those processes, but also to give some indication of points of concern in the assessment of a bereaved client. The assessment addresses a client's grief in the widest dimensions, relating to the spiritual, physical, intellectual, emotional and social elements of the client's world. Considering assessment in the context of bereavement counselling, the inevitable recurring question arises: can grief be measured? There are certainly scientific and statistical limitations on the measurement and assessment of grief, and I have a personal ambiguity about schemes and systems that may resound with echoes of comparisons and judgement, but there are aspects of families' lives that the counsellor may be aware of or need to discover which may enhance the picture of a client's grief. The assessment tool is also useful in discerning whether certain elements of the grieving process are at an acceptable or concerning level. This, however, may be strongly influenced by the counsellor's own preconceptions of grief experiences, which reiterates the necessity for grief counsellors to be fully aware of their own process and loss history. Ascertaining, for example, where 'normal' grief reactions (Humphrey and Zimpfer, 1996), such as tearfulness, sleeplessness and lack of motivation, develop into clinical depression is not a precise science. It will require reflexivity, purposeful supervision and, possibly, wider discussion with colleagues, which impinges on the even wider issue of confidentiality. However, it is an obligation of the responsible counsellor, with the GP, to assess where a client might benefit from drug therapy. The appropriate use of drug intervention to alleviate a clinical depression can facilitate a client's motivation to undertake the arduous task of grieving. Again, this is an area of negotiation within assessment and between counsellor and client. Many in society believe, rightly, that no drug intervention will take away the pain of grief but, returning to Lazarus' suggestion of misinformation, some clients benefit from a clearer understanding of aspects of depression and the realisation that clinical depression can, in itself, prevent a sufferer from grieving adequately. Appropriate drug therapy can sometimes enable, rather than mask, the grieving process. Liaison with a client's GP would, naturally, only take place with the prior knowledge and permission of the client. On the few occasions where my concerns for a client's mental and emotional health prompted communication with a GP (still with a client's foreknowledge), I sometimes queried internally whether I was being over-protective and disempowering my client. These situations are extremely difficult to gauge, but I reasoned that depression could be so enervating that a bereaved client lacks the energy and motivation to make the first contact with a GP. It is a paradox of depression that self-esteem can be sufficiently debilitated to convince the sufferer that they are unworthy of support and help—thereby not seeking the very relief they need. The autonomy of the client may occasionally be subservient to the danger of suicide.

The Grief Assessment profile might be more reminiscent of Lazarus than Rogers, but I perceive the concept of evaluating or assessing a client's wider contextual life-experiences—and thereby entering more fully into the client's frame of reference—as an effectively humanistic process.

Grief Assessment Profile

1. **The spiritual domain**

   a) *Belief systems*: what is the client's belief system? The counsellor must respect and value that system. Correct vocabulary: often effected by mirroring the language of the client—is a substantial basis for empathic relating.

   b) *Cultural background*: is it loss-accepting, ambivalent, loss-denying? Does this aid or complicate grief? Is the client 'allowed' to discuss loss? Feel sadness? Be angry?

   c) *Church or religious support*: does the client attend a place of worship? Is it a supportive or punitive environment?

   d) *Memorials*: does the client visit a grave, plaque or special place?

   Memorialisation is a crucial element in the grieving process, but the two extremes of creating a shrine or eliminating all reminders would be a cause for concern in grief assessment.

   Family members may well differ in all of the above, so the counsellor should endeavour to project empathic tolerance of all for the family to emulate.

2. **The physical domain**

   a) *Location*: is the client accessible or isolated: close to friends/transport/GP?

   b) *Health*: good, average or poor? Counsellors should be aware of any major health losses, such as menopause/hysterectomy; mastectomy; vasectomy; amputation.

c) *Appetite*: weight gain or loss? Three meals a day or 'little and often'? Sweet foods? Comfort eating?

d) *Sleep*: too little or too much? Is there a changed pattern? Does the client speak of dreams or nightmares?

e) *Exercise*: is the client physically active or lethargic? Motivated or utterly lacking in motivation?

f) *Hobbies and activities*: have social contacts continued or ceased? Continuity and stability are reassuring securities for the bereaved client.

3. **The intellectual domain**

a) *Age*

b) *Ability to express feelings*: does the client have the language and vocabulary to articulate their grief? One of the criticisms of talking therapies is that they can exclude those who struggle to verbalise their feelings and this is an area where perceptive use of counselling skills is paramount.

c) *Lifestage*: is the client in transition or stable? (Transitional stages could include adolescence, newly-married, divorcing, menopausal, retired or re-locating.)

d) *Ability to understand loss*: does the client have any learning difficulties? Are they mature or immature for their age?

e) *Reading/helpful literature*: does the client seek or require literature? Would they watch relevant videos?

Children's developmental cognitions of death and loss have been well documented (Worden, 1996, Herbert, 1996) and are addressed elsewhere in this volume, but the counsellor should remain aware that chronological age is not necessarily an accurate indication of emotional age.

4. **The emotional domain**

a) *Nature of the loss*: what was the client's relationship to the deceased prior to the death? Was it honest and open or secretive and colluding? What was the place and circumstance of the death? Were family members present?

b) *Grief history and successive losses*: the effect of loss is accumulative (Lendrum and Syme, 1992), and may include previous bereavements, health losses, redundancy, house moves, abusive childhood, infertility or adoption issues or disability.

c) *Complexity of the lost relationship*: was there sibling rivalry? Was it a love/hate relationship? Had divorce complicated the family relationships?

d) *Ability to tolerate and express feelings*: does the client give themself permission to grieve, or camouflage issues with platitudes or humour? Can they tolerate painful feelings or are they subjugated with alcohol, drugs, work or sleep?

e) *Capacity to trust others*: is the client withdrawn and guarded or candid and open? Do they have a history of being supported or disappointed in their relationships?

f) *Relationships*: does the client have at least one solid supportive relationship in their network?

5. **The social domain**

a) *Financial security or anxiety*: does a financial compulsion to work conflict with an emotional desire to remain at home?

b) *Employment situation*: is the client in receipt of a salary or state benefits? Is compassionate leave offered or is 'sick' leave the only viability? Is there any workplace counselling offered?

c)   *Isolated or seeking assistance*: is there a support structure in the client's social circle, and will the client utilise it?

d)   *Support network*: what does the genogram around the client consist of? Family, friends, GP, counsellor? Do family and friends endorse or deny the loss?

e)   *Extended family*: are they in touch, or 'lost'? Are the relationships comfortable or apparently cool and distant?

This basic tool provides an outline to a client's phenomenological perspective and, while not necessarily used in direct work with clients, can provide a surprisingly comprehensive overview of the situation when completed by the counsellor after even an initial visit. The aspects considered in the profile include those areas that clients are often voluble and forthcoming about, and even the withdrawn or inarticulate client will provide substantial answers for the assessing counsellor.

Some knowledge of the wider context of a client's life is certainly helpful, but completely redundant in a vacuum. It must be reiterated that the therapeutic alliance between counsellor and bereaved client flourishes within an environment of warmth and empathy, not clinical detachment. 'Being with' a client requires more than a cerebral understanding of their situation. Rogers, reflecting on his 'presence' with clients, wrote shortly before his death, 'At those moments it seems that my inner spirit has reached out and touched the spirit of the other' (Dryden, 1996).

It is this depth of intuitive response that should be the hallmark of a caring and productive counselling relationship.

Counsellors or carers wishing to offer bereavement support would do well to question their personal motivation for entering this arena. It is crucial in all fields of counselling for the practitioner to be aware of their own idiosyncrasies, strengths and weaknesses. In bereavement support, particularly, the astute professional will have examined their own experiences of loss, grief and change to ensure that there are no residual issues finding secondary comfort in the story of a client. Needless to say, it would be both foolish and unethical to operate in this demanding area without the reflexive and sustaining provision of adequate professional supervision.

References

Angus L, Levitt H, Hardtke K (1999)The narrative process coding system: research applications and implications for psychotherapy practice. *J Clin Psychol* **55**: 1255–70

Audet C, Everall RD (2003) Counsellor self-disclosure: client-informed implications for practice. *Counsel Psychother Res* **3**: 223–31

Beck AT (1976) *Cognitive Therapy and the Emotional Disorders*. International Universities Press, New York

Dryden W (1996) *Handbook of Individual Therapy*. Sage, London

Dryden W (1991) *A Dialogue with Arnold Lazarus*. Open University Press, Buckingham

Edwards CE, Murdock NL (1994) Characteristics of therapists self-disclosure in the counselling process. *J Counsel Devel* **72**: 384–89

Ellis A (1989) The history of cognition in psychotherapy. In: Freeman A, Simon KM, Beutler LE, Arkowitz H, eds. *Comprehensive Handbook of Cognitive Therapy*. Plenum Press, New York

Fiedler FE (1950)A comparison of therapeutic relationships in psychoanalytic, non-directive and Adlerian therapy. *J Counsel Psychol* **14**: 436–45

Herbert M (1996) *Supporting Bereaved and Dying Children and their Parents*. BPS Books, Leicester

Humphrey GM, Zimpfer D (1996) *Counselling for Grief and Bereavement*. Sage, London

Jacobs M (2002) *Psychodynamic Counselling in Action*. Sage, London

Klass D (1999) *The Spiritual Lives of Bereaved Parents*. Taylor Francis, Philadelphia

Kopp S (1972) *If You Meet the Buddha on the Road, Kill Him*. Sheldon Press, London

Kuykendall J (1998) Oral Presentation London

Lazarus AA (1995)Multimodal counselling. In: Nelson-Jones R, ed. *The Theory and Practice of Counselling*. Cassell, London

Lendrum S, Syme G (1992) *The Gift of Tears*. Routledge, London

Machin L (1998) Grief counselling in context: multiple roles and professional compromise. *Br J Guid Counsel* **26**: ??page nos??

Machin L, Spall R (2004)Mapping grief: a study in practice using a quantitative and qualitative approach to exploring and addressing the range of responses to loss. *Counsel Psychother Res* **4**: 9–17

McLeod J (1997) *Narrative and Psychotherapy*. Sage, London

McLeod J, Machin L (1998) The context of counselling: a neglected dimension of training, research and practice. *Br J Guid Counsel* **26**: 325

Mearns D (1994) *Developing Person-Centred Counselling*. Sage, London

Meier A (2002) Narrative in psychotherapy theory, practice and research: a critical review. *Counsel Psychother Res* **2**: 239–51

Neimeyer RA, Anderson A (2002)Meaning Reconstruction Theory. In: Thompson, N, ed. *Loss and Grief*. Palgrave, Basingstoke

Nelson-Jones R (1999) Towards cognitive/humanistic counselling. *Counselling* **10**: 913

Nelson-Jones R (1995) *The Theory and Practice of Counselling*. Cassell, London

Newton M (2002) *Savage Girls and Wild Boys*. Faber and Faber, London

Parkes CM (2000)Counselling bereaved people—help or harm? *Bereavement Care* **19**: 19–21

Parkes CM, Relf M, Couldrick A (1996) *Counselling in Terminal Care and Bereavement*. BPS Books, Leicester

Rochford G (1991) Theory, concepts, feelings and practice: The contemplation of bereavement within a social work course. In: Lishman J, ed. *Handbook of Theory for Practice Teachers in Social Work*. Jessica Kingsley, London

Rogers C (1978) *On Personal Power*. Constable, London

Rogers C (1961) *On Becoming a Person*. Constable, London

Rosenblatt PC (2000) *Parent Grief: Narratives of Loss and Relationship*. Brunner/Mazel, Philadelphia

Spong S, Hollanders H (2003) Cognitive therapy and social power. *Counsel Psychother Res* **3** 216–22

Thorne B (1996) Person-centred counselling. In: Dryden W, ed. *A Handbook of Individual Therapy*. Sage, London

Worden JW (1996) *Children and Grief*. Guildford Press, New York

Wosket V (1999) *The Therapeutic Use of Self*. Routledge, London

3

Supporting bereaved children

The two recurring themes when communicating with bereaved or dying children are 'permission' and 'honesty'. Children and young people need to sense, with clarity and sincerity, that they have permission to ask whatever they need to ask, permission to feel whatever they are feeling and permission to regress or progress according to their own timescale.

Those who support bereaved children and young people will encounter a challenging but fulfilling role that requires thorough preparation and self-examination. Supporters must provide honesty in their responses, honesty in their personal self-awareness and a genuine concern for the youngsters with whom they are working. It is incumbent upon supporters of children to take this self-assessment seriously, because children and young people will soon recognise a fraud. In giving children permission to ask their questions, practitioners will need to demonstrate their own openness to candid enquiry, ensuring that no responses occur that offer a covert judgemental theme. Children will, of course, ask some bizarre questions at times ('Why are there hairs in your nose?') totally unrelated to the anticipated topic, but that, too, can be a defence mechanism and needs to be calmly accommodated by the discerning practitioner. Defence mechanisms and avoidance strategies serve their purpose of course, so it is not the remit of the bereavement supporter to brazenly dismantle these structures, but to journey alongside a child while they circumnavigate their thoughts and feelings and offer adults they trust an occasional insight.

It is not possible to set a fixed timescale for grieving in children, just as it is not possible for adults, but the first two years following the death of someone close are likely to evidence the greatest impact of the loss. My reluctance to set chronological limits to grief is compounded by the realisation that many bereaved children can manifest reactions to loss and trauma some time after the event, particularly if grief issues were unaddressed at the time of the loss. It is naïve to assume that a child must be 'recovered' or 'unaffected' simply because of the passage of time. As we become increasingly conversant with influences upon child development, it would seem imprudent to ignore the impact of loss and change on the lives of children and young people. While there have been those who would dispute the need for bereavement support interventions for children (Harrington and Harrison, 1999), it is preferable to err on the side of prevention and assume that a support intervention that is possibly unnecessary is likely to be less harmful to a bereaved child than a dearth of vital provision and understanding.

Children, naturally, have their own developmental process to contend with, in addition to any grief issues they may encounter, so there are likely to be differences in the ways children grieve at varying stages in their life. Conversely, chronological age is only an approximate guide to a child's emotional and intellectual development so the following divisions may be approached with flexibility and sensitivity and, hopefully, a deeper understanding of individual children with whom we are working.

Developmental cognition

Zero to two years

Babies clearly have a very limited vocabulary and no concept of death or permanence. However, they can sense loss although if that loss is through bereavement then that finality will dawn very slowly as their intellect and comprehension mature. For the babe-in-arms, there is little experiential differentiation between their mother leaving the house for two hours or forever, except for the increasing timescale. The protestation at the absence of a familiar figure will be very similar (Bowlby, 1969). The most valuable therapeutic intervention afforded to this very young age group is dependent upon the same factor in each circumstance— the quality of the substitute care they receive. Most babies who are temporarily 'abandoned' by their mother for a few hours will manage to move from protestation to an acceptance of their substitute carer and may even progress beyond grudging acceptance to a delighted satisfaction with their new carer. This situation will be similar, even where death is the cause of a permanent absence. Babies are more likely to be affected by the death of a parent than the death of a sibling, given the baby's highly dependent status. They will, however, be attuned to the atmosphere in a house of mourning and possibly respond fractiously. Bending notes that babies from six months may react to the absence of their primary carer with irritability and changes to their sleeping, eating and crying patterns (Bending, 1993). The greatest difficulty in supporting an infant through bereavement is that the surviving carer—whether they have been bereaved of a partner or a child—will be temporarily debilitated in their parenting skills and preoccupied with their own grief. Indeed, supporting a baby through bereavement is tantamount to supporting their carer.

Early years

Children from about three to six years of age are likely to be prelogical and egocentric in their thinking, often termed the 'magical thinking' stage (Piaget, 1929) as children at this stage believe the world revolves around them and they, and their thoughts, hold power within that world. Wishes can come true and the tooth fairy is still a reality for this age group. It is a truly magical stage in child development and a delight to encounter. Sadly, the difficulty for children experiencing bereavement at this stage is that they may have a profound sense of causality or self-blame—particularly in sibling or parental loss where the relationship might have been ambivalent and the surviving child blames his or her own 'naughtiness' or resentful feelings for the death.

While children of this age are beginning to recognise, use and understand the words 'dead' and 'death', their conceptualisation of death is inevitably immature. They cannot conceive of the finality of death; they simply have not lived long enough to have any perception of 'foreverness'. Thus, the child in this stage who is carefully informed about their father's death in a car accident, is involved in and attends the funeral, and appears to have a grasp of the sorry situation, may yet, six months later, enquire brightly, 'So, is Daddy coming home now?' Not only is it impossible to impose this understanding upon an immature mind, but it is also a heart-rending stage for a grieving parent who is prevailed upon for patient repetition of the facts until the child has sufficient conceptualisation of the permanence of death. Clichéd though it may seem, children do tend to develop a natural concept of the permanence of death through the loss of pets, or the understanding that a wasp, once swatted, is not going to return to life. For this reason, it is helpful for schools and other social arenas to include the topic of death so that children's burgeoning curiosity can accommodate such issues, hopefully *before* a child has to encounter the painful reality of a close bereavement. Despite the 'magic' of this stage, bereaved children are most aided by factual and truthful explanations, with as little embroidery as possible. There is an understandable inclination within adults speaking to young children about death to utilise euphemisms such as 'gone away', 'not coming back', 'in Heaven' and so on. The worst offender, of course, is 'gone to sleep for a long, long time'. Naturally, children who hear such explanations will have their reservations about going to sleep. Simple, straightforward language is best, and there is no disgrace in responding with 'I don't know' to a child's question, if you truly do not know. If a child asked me what 'being dead' or 'Heaven' was like, I would be obliged to reply that I did not know, but we could wonder about how we *imagined* it to be. Children welcome honesty and are quite prepared to share in our musings about the unknown from quite an early age. Children of this age may also regress to an earlier stage of their growth, for example developing enuresis or becoming more tactile. This is a natural response to trauma and temporary indulgence is likely to elicit a healthier response than reprimands.

Seven to eleven years

This is known as the 'concrete thinking' stage as children become more aware of finality, permanence and death. It is the age at which children naturally consolidate their understanding of death through their developmental experiences. The death of a sibling is, I feel, especially tragic at this stage because individuals, while understanding *about* death, do not normally consider their own mortality until much later in life. The death of a peer brings a premature encounter with such considerations, which can be very unnerving and unsettling for youngsters. Children of this age, and younger, may well experience some separation anxiety whereby they become overanxious during even customary, short separations from a loved one. School avoidance is a possible response to these anxieties. Resolution of separation anxieties takes time, as only the repeated assurance of safe returns will gradually diminish the child's apprehension. Bereavement within this age range can produce very serious little people who sadly had a carefree childhood abruptly sabotaged. Disturbed behaviour would not be unusual and schools may often comment on the changed personality in a child of this age who has been bereaved. It is helpful to consider any unsocial behaviour as a normal response to an abnormal situation (Herbert, 1996) and remember the tacit 'permission' that allows children to react naturally to an overwhelming circumstance. In contrast, bereaved children at this stage may also develop an empathic consideration for their peers that can produce an exceptionally charming and popular child.

Adolescence

Teenagers can have confused feelings at the best of times, so to add bereavement to the steaming cauldron of their emotions brings additional complications. Adolescents are going through the process of 'losing' their childhood too, so may have become withdrawn and uncommunicative even prior to bereavement. This is an age where youngsters may seriously consider their spirituality and 'the meaning of life', and these considerations will be thrown into disarray by the death of someone close to them. Honesty and permission continue to be the mainstay of support initiatives with this age group. Adolescents are particularly well attuned to deception and hypocrisy and will despise those whose support efforts are seen to lack sincerity. Approaches to the uncommunicative adolescent can often be made via music, TV or sport, each of which can ultimately create the fertile ground in which to broach more reflective feelings. Studies have reflected a medium-term association between childhood bereavement and academic achievement (Abdelnoor and Hollins, 2004) and, given the intellectual demands of this stage of life, it is clear that some consideration should be given to the impact of bereavement and support mechanisms that might be instated. Abdelnoor and Hollins conclude, in their paper, that the effect of bereavement may be prolonged and that young people might need intermittent support throughout secondary and tertiary education.

This is an age of extremes of emotion, ambition and dependence, and assumptions can often be made regarding a young person's maturity that may be quite erroneous. The opposing dangers of smothering or neglecting must be guarded against, although that is undoubtedly far easier to write than enact.

There are generalised reactions to grief and loss that may be seen in children and young people across varying ages. Actually, these responses to bereavement are not dissimilar in adults—another reminder of the childlikeness of grief:

- Sleeping difficulties

- Eating problems

(each of the above becomes a problem at either end of the 'too little or too much' spectrum, although some temporary disruption of normal patterns is so commonplace as to be considered a normal response)

- Susceptibility to infection

- Imagined illnesses or symptoms

- Regression

- Separation anxiety

- Sadness, anger, fear, guilt, resentment

- Lack of motivation.

Supporting grieving children is a long-term task with no simple or instantaneous solutions. However, it is not such an onerous undertaking that it merits the trepidation of adults with which it is often contemplated. There are some basic guidelines that offer a framework to all bereavement support, but particularly apply to work with children. Supporters should:

- Be honest in their exchanges with young people

- Give permission for all and any feelings to be expressed (not simply the 'acceptable' ones)

- Allow children to ask questions. Adults should respond thoughtfully, taking care to answer at the level of the child's enquiry. Try not to give a child more information than they are seeking at that moment

- Endeavour not to be shocked by anything a child might share with you. The expressed surprise or horror of an adult will stifle any further dialogue with the child.

- Utilise resources—books, games, music, films. There is a plethora of resources (some recommendations are in the Appendix) that can be adapted for use in bereavement support and encourage discussion.

For too long, children were assumed to be unaffected by loss and grief. Their natural resilience was, and still is, cited as a substitute for more formal bereavement support interventions (Barnard *et al*, 1999). Children do, indeed, have a natural resilience and an innate ability to transcend traumatic situations at times. They will maintain their childlike capacity for flitting between moods. Frequently, their concentration span is not sufficiently developed to grieve visibly for long periods. Quite frankly, children get bored with grief and can often bring light relief to the sombre adults around them. None of this, however, justifies an abdication of our responsibility to offer some level of support to a bereaved child. A child who is validated as a griever can begin to rebuild and restructure their self-esteem, can grow in understanding of self and others, can process, rather than stifle or delay, their grief. A child whose grief is acknowledged and accepted will no longer have to subjugate feelings, which may then take a more devious route to expression, sometimes necessitating psychological, psychiatric or even legislative interventions.

Supporting bereaved children should not be an option, it should be compulsory. That is not to imply formal, structured programmes are necessary for each and every bereaved child. Degrees of provision and intervention will range from perfectly adequate family and social support structures, to planned programmes and professional assistance. While many children may not need formal or specialised help, the facilities should still be available and accessible to all children. The Childhood Bereavement Network (www.cbn@ncb.org.uk) is an umbrella organisation that is striving to compile and maintain a functional directory of organisations throughout the UK who are offering bereavement support to children and young people. This is, in itself, indicative of the transformation in attitudes to childhood bereavement and offers hope for a future where bereaved children and young people will not have to experience the isolation and suppression of former years.

How schools can help

Every school will inevitably encounter bereaved children, but the topic is seldom addressed directly unless a pupil or member of staff dies. In those instances, memorialisation is likely to be the key initiative with trees planted, plaques established, poems written and remembrance services attended. All such activities have their place and can be beneficial to a grieving school community. However, there is a much wider issue to be addressed in that the education curriculum has only latterly begun to address issues of death and dying, with a continuing aversion on the part of many practitioners to imbed that curriculum in the daily lives of children and young people. With the current emphasis on continuing professional development, teachers could be encouraged to enhance their pastoral skills with training specific to understanding children's responses to loss, change and grief. Experience has taught us that a coy reluctance to address the facts of life over previous decades did nothing to reduce the UK's shameful record of teenage pregnancies. Knowledge is power, and those countries where attitudes to sex are more overtly educative reflect corresponding levels of understanding and reason in their young people. There is a parallel between these attitudes and those towards death and bereavement issues and it is suggested that the facts of death should take equal prominence in our curricula, which would have the result of enabling future generations to comprehend and attend to circumstances of grief and loss with a wider repertoire of skills. Indeed, it could be argued that the facts of death should carry a greater imperative than the facts of life; for while reproduction is a possible event in the futures of schoolchildren, bereavement is a certainty and may well occur much earlier in their school life.

It is understandable that teachers and other school staff should feel hesitant about addressing the topic of death. They simply reflect the cultural norms of our society as this final taboo is grappled with. There is, however, an encouraging movement towards articulating the hitherto unspoken concerns, and ensuring that bereaved children are at least directed towards some sort of support initiative, even if that lies outside the school structure. Organisations such as *Winston's Wish* (Stokes and Crossley, 1995) and *Rainbows* (Yehl Marta, 2004) can offer a service to bereaved children and young people. Similarly, practitioners from a local children's hospice, Macmillan nurses, Marie Curie nurses, social workers, community police teams—even funeral directors—have been known to visit schools to offer their unique perspective and some helpful insight into the topic of bereavement.

External or in-service training opportunities are likely to be required by many educationalists who tend to shy away from the topic of death unless they are given additional support (Brown, 1999). Nevertheless, from the very earliest stages of the Foundation Stage, through to completion of secondary school, the curriculum already possesses a framework that could readily incorporate a more natural approach to death as a part of life. Within Early Years education, the areas of learning lend themselves to the inclusion of death in the curriculum (with the possible exception of mathematical development, although an imaginative practitioner could surely include some relevant numeracy as well).

Areas of learning

- *Personal, social and emotional development*: probably the most obvious section in which to address issues of loss, change and grief. PSE is, in itself, expected to carry a cross-curricular element as children learn to be confident, caring and considerate individuals (Dowling, 2000). Historically, emotional development was probably considered to be beyond the remit of an academic institution, but increasingly, understanding of multiple intelligence and emotional literacy (Gardner, 1993) has brought greater significance to this area of learning.

- *Communication, language and literacy*: given that much of a child's confusion surrounding death lies in the perplexing veiled language utilised by adults, an exploration of the vocabulary of loss and death would not be inappropriate. As suggested in subsequent chapters, the fear that can be manifest in adults' avoidance of conversations about death with children is often located in the absence of a functional vocabulary. However, useful analogies and resources can be found in the everyday minutiae of life and may create far more natural opportunities for discourse than a stilted encounter informed by a textbook. Equally, a child's descriptive spoken or written narrative of their experiences often helps to create and re-create a story that will enhance the child's understanding of a particular situation.

  When stories of loss, change or death can be incorporated into school life alongside the traditional tales of 'what I did at the weekend', then we shall be encouraging a future society that can become far more articulate and comfortable with death issues than previous generations. A burgeoning supply of useful literary resources is also available (see Appendix) that can introduce the topic of death or loss and change to children in a familiar, habitual way

- *Knowledge and understanding of the world*: from local exploration to multicultural practices, children can investigate differing attitudes and responsibilities around death. From the card shop to the church, to the local press, links to the topic can be established and the ubiquitous nature of death and change acknowledged in an objective and unambiguous way

- *Physical development*: growth is, appropriately, affirmed more than decline, and for children at the start of their lives it should be no other way. The cycle of growth in nature (well depicted through growing sunflowers) can convey something of change and adaptation to children without a sense of morbidity. Growth, fruition, nutrition and health are actually quite natural arenas for death to also appear within the topic; and it is this commonplace acceptance of life's cycle that will ease the discomfort previously felt around a 'morbid' subject

- *Creative development*: children can be extremely expressive through their creativity and this is often an outlet for emotional concerns that may remain unspoken. Representation through drawing, painting, and modelling offers methods of expression that may be less inhibited than in other areas of the curriculum.

School can be a reassuringly familiar place for bereaved youngsters, but it may also be a place where much of their grief is expressed. The pressure within a grieving household may be such that the school day is greeted with relief by children desperately seeking some familiar 'normality' in their life. While the accustomed school routine and friendships may well be a source of comfort to the child, there is a danger that school staff utilise this concept as a reason to not address the loss. This is typical of the fine lines drawn around these issues and staff should undertake to allow the comfort of 'normality', yet acknowledge the import of a child's recent bereavement. Youngsters who are reluctant to add to the sadness and pain at home may express their grief through unusual behaviour at school. The Jungian concept of *shadow* offers a reminder that those issues which cannot be verbally expressed may be behaviourally acted out. If neither school nor home can contain the grief of a child, where is that grief to go— and what will be the psychological ramifications for the child?

Unfortunately, it is not always easy for teachers and classroom assistants to recognise the grieving child. In younger children, especially, their shorter concentration span leads them to dip in and out of sadness for relatively brief episodes, so their grief may be overlooked. This is a very natural way for young children to live alongside their grief, but presents obvious difficulties for the practitioner who is endeavouring to offer support at the right time. An acknowledgement of the child's loss is an initial necessity, laying the foundations for any future encounters.

It is helpful to liaise with a family, where possible, assuring them of a school's support and empathy, but also establishing the approach to take. Whenever a family and the bereaved young person are agreeable, it is preferable for a child's peers at school to be forewarned about a post-bereavement return to the classroom. Acknowledging a young person's loss need not be prolonged, emotive or sentimental, but ignoring it altogether is more likely to provoke distress and frustration in the child. Cards may be sent and preparations may be made for receiving the bereaved child back into a supportive peer group, but the most beneficial influence will be the school's ethos and its implementation of death education. If pupils are already in possession of an adequate vocabulary, have already stretched their personal, social and emotional understanding to incorporate compassion and empathy, have a concept of death as a part of life, then the preparatory work has been done and the grieving child should be cushioned within an informed and sensitive environment.

Within the educational setting, there are several pitfalls to be aware of:

- Some topics may be poignantly sensitive, such as 'My Family', 'Christmas' and other festivals, 'Holidays' and others. The considerate practitioner will foresee such hurdles and be prepared for a quiet discussion with a bereaved pupil

- As with adults, grief may take some time to surface, but school life moves on rapidly, so a pupil's 'uncharacteristic' behaviour may not be traced back and associated with a bereavement. Communication between teachers is vital, particularly following the long summer break and a change of classroom. A child bereaved in May could well be exhibiting the worst effects of their bereavement in September/October, yet be with a teacher who knew very little of the previous school year's traumas

- Children may feel isolated as their peers struggle to comprehend this unfamiliar territory. Isolated children are more at risk of bullying, school phobia and poor attendance so it is a situation requiring close monitoring

- In bereaved children, as well as adults, concentration may be disrupted for some time. Children may not be personally aware of this and may not realise how often they are distracted or day-dreaming. Teachers should endeavour not to reproach bereaved pupils for such behaviour as it is beyond the control of both bereaved adults and children, and will only subside over time

- It is not unusual for youngsters to regress and exhibit behaviour more associated with earlier years. This, too, is more likely to decrease in response to tolerant acceptance rather than rebuke

- Paradoxically, bereaved children have undoubtedly had this premature encounter with the fragility of life and may sometimes display an emotional maturity beyond their years

- In the loss of a sibling, some young people struggle to over-achieve in order to compensate for their parent's loss. Conversely, a previously bright pupil may lose motivation when the core of life's meaning has been so painfully challenged.

In conclusion, schools that strive to offer a supportive environment to their bereaved pupils should revisit the above principles of *permission* and *honesty*, adding to those, *communication*. Communication within the school, communication between school and family, and paraprofessional and multi-agency communication where required, will establish an informed but sensitive setting where a bereaved child can be reassured and nurtured.

The school that can address death education as a universal topic prior to it becoming an individual reality is best prepared to create a sustaining environment for those pupils who will encounter grief and loss within their school lifetime.

References

Abdelnoor A, Hollins S (2004) The effect of childhood bereavement on secondary school performance. *Educ Psychol Pract* **20**: 43–54

Barnard P, Barnard I, Barnard M, Nagy J (1999) *Children, Bereavement and Trauma: Nurturing Resilience*. Jessica Kingsley Publishers, London

Bending M (1993) *Caring for Bereaved Children*. Cruse Bereavement Care, Richmond

Bowlby J (1969) *Attachment and Loss*. Basic Books, New York

Brown E (1999) *Loss, Change and Grief*. David Fulton, London

Dowling M (2000) *Young Children's Personal, Social and Emotional Development*. Sage, London

Gardner H (1993) *Frames of Mind*. Fontana, London

Harrington R, Harrison L (1999) Unproven assumptions about the impact of bereavement on children. *J R Soc Med* **92**: 230–33

Herbert M (1996) *Supporting Bereaved and Dying Children and their Parents*. BPS Books, Leicester

Piaget J (1929) *The Child's Conception of the World*. Routledge, London

Stokes J, Crossley D (1995) Camp Winston: a residential intervention with bereaved children. In: Smith S C, Pennells M, eds. *Interventions with Bereaved Children*. Jessica Kingsley, London

Yehl Marta S (2004) *Healing the Hurt, Restoring the Hope*. Rodale, London

Section II

Practical Applications

4

Children and death

'A sigh is something your heart says that your head doesn't understand'

Thus spoke a six-year-old sage who regularly amazed me with his insight and youthful wisdom. At the age of six, he prematurely entered an adult world of grief and bereavement after the sad death of his younger brother. On the morning of his brother's death, we collected conkers together in the grounds of the children's hospice, nature's windfalls giving timely symbolism to the disposal of 'shells' no longer required—and so we talked of his brother's impending funeral.

Children have a remarkable capacity to discuss and understand some of life's profundities, if the adults around them can accommodate a child's vocabulary and limited experience. It is recognised that children who experience severe illness and hospitalisation can seem mature beyond their years (Bluebond-Langner, 1978) and I suspect that may be apparent also in the siblings of dying children.

The same six-year-old sage suggested, when reflecting on life after death, that perhaps we are all in Heaven, dreaming we're alive, and then we wake up—adding that perhaps God woke his little brother early because he was having nightmares. I was left pondering this possibility for some time and considered the conversations this small philosopher might have had with Nietzsche or Wittgenstein.

Children, even dying or bereaved children, have a right to their childhood and the children's hospice movement evolved out of that very premise. Neither hospitals nor adult hospices would be the preference of families caring for a terminally ill child, yet wanting them still to be surrounded with the accoutrements of childhood. Some families will prefer to care for their child at home and, with the support of home care services, may be enabled to do that. Others, however, will choose the respite and sensitive professional support offered within the children's hospice. In whichever case, family-centred care will be provided and every effort will be made to ensure the dying child is allowed their entitlement to carefree childhood for as long as possible. But, of course it is not free of care. The foreboding and sorrow of a terminal prognosis lurk in the shadows, and for some children their recognition and acknowledgement come as a relief from subterfuge or silence. I am not advocating that *all* terminally ill children, in *all* circumstances, should be informed of their impending death. I well recall a mother who despised the thought of deceiving her sick child, yet understood, too, that an explanation that included going *anywhere* without her parents would be confusing and distressing for her small daughter. Frank and direct discussions must always be considered against the broader backdrop of a child's character, maturity and experience. As Elizabeth Kubler-Ross said, 'Although all patients have the *right* to know, not all patients have the *need* to know' (Kubler-Ross, 1983).

Nevertheless, it would seem that many children approaching death have an innate sense of leaving, often accepted with a philosophical but unspoken serenity that bemuses the adults around them. The artwork of dying children has been noted to include images of sky or departure, such as aeroplanes, birds, rainbows or angels (Bertoia, 1993). Other authors have suggested that it is increasingly evident that many children know more than it is believed they know (Bluebond-Langner, 1999; Farrell, 1999). Farrell adds that '*dying children have a need to ask, to know, and to understand about death and dying*' (ibid). One young girl created an entire fantasy land through words and pictures that not only contained humour and remarkable imaginative prose, but also some astute analogies of the challenges of life and death.

A four-year-old girl who, at the time, was in a hopeful stage of remission, went on holiday with her family. While sat on a beach she turned to her grandfather and said, 'Grandad, you'll have to find another little girl to sit on your knee.' Within weeks she relapsed and died. Was it a chance remark? Was it meaningless? Or is there an intuitive comprehension that those of us who are not near to death have not yet experienced? Anecdotal evidence from both child and adult deaths has often implied an unspoken awareness, on the part of the one who was dying, of their imminent departure; desks have been tidied, projects completed, letters written, conversations held which all offer a retrospective fascination in their unwitting relevance to future events. Naturally, there are many situations where untimely death interrupts a vivacious existence with an abruptness that leaves mourners reeling with disbelief. Yet even some of those circumstances ultimately extract meaning from an apparently meaningless event. Other narratives from terminally ill children and their families contribute to the conjecture.

A seven-year-old boy, vacillating over a choice of books for me to read to him, after I nonchalantly stated he had 'all the time in the world' to choose one, solemnly responded, 'You haven't you know, you've only got the time until you die.' He died days later.

A five-year-old girl roused herself sleepily from the sofa in her parents' home and said, 'I'll just go with my hair like this, Mum.' Then, a few minutes later, 'I'll be off now then.' She died that night.

An eleven-year-old girl, aware of the relevance of anniversaries, was determined not to die on a friend's wedding day, or any significant birthdays. She asked her mother, 'Is today anything special, Mum?' and, reassured that it was not, died that day.

For all those children who overtly or covertly referred to their approaching death, or made uncanny references to their imminent departure, there were many more whose death was a silent drift into unconsciousness, or others who struggled and challenged to the bitter end, some even defying their prognosis with a longer lifespan than anyone anticipated. To elevate the experience of child death to a suggestion where suffering is unknown and kindly death comes with grace and beneficence to each child would be a travesty of all that families endure, and practitioners strive to accomplish, in the arena of paediatric palliative care. Pain relief in terminally ill children owes much of its evolution to the expertise and operational implementation afforded by the children's hospice movement and it is rare for a child to suffer unrelenting pain. However, the psychological pain of isolation, uncertainty and fear cannot always be alleviated through pharmacological intervention. Some of my conversations with dying youngsters exemplified this.

Adolescents can be very astute and articulate in their assessments of people and life, but are equally capable of being withdrawn and silent. Danai Papadatou once likened adolescents to lobsters who must lose one shell during their development and are particularly vulnerable until they have grown a new shell (Papadatou, 1999). Consider then the additional vulnerability of the dying adolescent who is caught in the paradox of withdrawing from life while needing to belong. The customary identity crises of teenage years are compounded by the integration of both a living and a dying self. Teenagers are sometimes able to balance remarkably well the dilemma of preparing for death while investing in life.

Philip was very aware of his terminal prognosis and wanted to discuss his funeral with me. He also wanted his family—specifically, his mother—to know that he was aware of his imminent death. Although he knew that he and his mother could never contemplate such a painful conversation, I was to be the intermediary in order that a tacit understanding might exist between them. He typified those young people who feel the need to protect their families from as much emotional pain as possible, even in some instances perpetuating the charade of a recovery to comply with the family myth. Such facades are not to be denigrated nor simplistically dismissed as denial. Hope and hypothesis for the future can sit realistically alongside awareness of degeneration and limitation—particularly for the dying adolescent, who will utilise whichever coping mechanism is appropriate in the perpetual conflict between maturity and decline. It was not unusual for a group of teenage boys, all suffering from a similar neuromuscular degenerative condition, to contemplate who of their number might next succumb fatally to their inevitable prognosis, while at the same time they could discuss university and career plans. This is not madness but exquisite sanity, for those who live daily with the knowledge of premature death are most aware that they must also immerse themselves in life.

Philip also contemplated the likely circumstances of his death. His worst fear was to choke to death—a not unreasonable fear given the condition from which he suffered—and there could be no absolute assurance that it would not be so. He admired some of the writings of Kahlil Gibran in *The Prophet*, who wrote a particular section on death:

> *For what is it to die, but to stand naked in the wind and to melt into the sun?*
> *And what is it to cease breathing but to free the breath from its restless tides,*
> *That it might rise and expand and seek God unencumbered?*
>
> (Gibran, 1991)

This was part of a passage Philip asked me to read at his funeral, but it also caused him to muse, 'perhaps not having to breathe will be absolute freedom.'

When I asked him how he endured the degenerative nature of his condition, having become increasingly disabled throughout his life, he replied that, as he could do less, he enjoyed more. He explained that the limitations of his activities caused him to invest more pleasure and satisfaction in those pursuits he could maintain, which ultimately became music and film. Two oncologists working with the Christie Hospital in Manchester conducted a study into the experiences of young people with recurrent or metastatic cancer and they, too, discovered, alongside some anger and anxiety, that many youngsters accepted their illness as part of life and were remarkably philosophical (Hodgson and Eden, 2003). I find it difficult, as well as humbling, to comprehend the lack of bitterness in such an attitude and was much relieved when Philip was at least compensated with a peaceful death devoid of choking episodes.

John experienced a crisis that convinced him, his family and the medical team that his death was imminent, then rallied and was relatively 'well' for another few weeks. He asked to speak to me because he was afraid. He stated simply, 'I thought I was dying but I didn't. If that wasn't dying, what will it be like?' Of course, I had no answer, but we were at least able to contemplate his fears and consider other matters that weighed upon him in his final days. As was so common, he particularly wanted his mother to know how much he loved her and was thankful for her years of care. There was a song he wanted to play to her—Whitney

Houston singing '*The greatest love of all*'—and we managed to locate a copy and leave him and his mum to listen and weep together. The song contains the line, 'no matter what they take from me, they can't take away my dignity' and it continues to remind me of the dignity with which young people could often encounter and tackle issues that many an older person would shy away from. John also decided, having been given a temporary reprieve from death, that now was the time to risk a few new challenges. He had never swum in his life and was quite fearful of doing so, but he ventured into the hydrotherapy pool at the hospice and enjoyed it. He even extended his culinary experiences by eating chicken for the first time in his life—and enjoyed it. When he eventually did die (and, yes, it was a peaceful death), he had said all he wanted to say and achieved the limited challenges he had set himself for those final weeks. He had voiced his hopes and his fears, some of which drew a practical response: 'a voice can only become significant when it is listened to and acted upon' (Oliviere and Monroe, 2003).

I recall a young boy who was not particularly gregarious or talkative, yet participated in hospice activities and enjoyed the companionship of other youngsters. Although he had a degenerative condition and his ultimate prognosis was certain, he died rather sooner and more suddenly than expected. Some weeks later, various items of fired pottery that youngsters had created were returned to the hospice, including one this young man had produced—it was the figure of a young boy with one arm raised, as if in farewell.

I can still smile at the remembrance of an enthusiastic three-year-old bottom-shuffler, who, with his limited mobility and purportedly no vision could nevertheless sense an open door immediately and would shuffle determinedly towards his newest escape route. If it's open, I must be expected to go through it… Such was his philosophy, and that sense of fearless adventure left a legacy with his family and others that continues to pervade their attitude to life. Every life leaves its trace.

A teenage girl, seeking some diversion, helped me compile a photo album from the Treasure Weekend that had recently been held. Curious about the photographs, she enquired about the activities and I explained the weekend was for bereaved brothers and sisters, to do some remembering, but also to have some fun. She was quietly amused and exultant that she knew so much about her brother and sister's future activities long before her own demise qualified them for attendance. She doggedly pursued further enquires about bereavement support, wanting to know how I would support her parents. She became acquainted with the Stepping Stones programme and seemed curiously reassured by the knowledge.

Bereaved siblings, too, offered their fair share of wisdom and natural curiosity. The hospice has a special bedroom (the Sunflower Room) that can be maintained at a lower temperature so that a child who has died can remain there, in bed, up until the funeral. This enables families to spend time with their child and somehow the repeated visits to a body that no longer has life in it can bring understanding and acceptance to even very young siblings. There seems to be an almost intuitive perception that this is not sleep; this is something different; and I appreciate the traditional time lapse that is often customary practice between death and the funeral for it is these few days that offer a deepening comprehension to younger, as well as older, members of the family. Some cultures, of course, preclude such a time lapse in their death and funeral rituals, and no doubt children from such cultures find other ways of comprehending the incomprehensible, but I am inclined to believe that viewing the body and being included in funeral rituals is helpful to children of all ages.

Conversations with bereaved siblings could fluctuate rapidly—like the mood swings of a child—between hilarity and sadness, and it is essential for the adult to follow, rather than direct, in these encounters (Herbert, 1996). One young girl asked if it was acceptable to love your grandmother more than your mother (ambivalent feelings were an overriding symptom of her grief).

A young boy sat on the floor with me, drawing a picture of the swimming pool as we talked about his loss. His picture, on completion, revealed a pool full of bright activity and laughing children. Yet he, in the picture, was tiny and out of all proportion to the other figures—a revealing insight into how small and vulnerable he was feeling.

However, another little girl, participating in a self-portrait activity that I had reluctantly joined commented that my self-portrait was not very good. I agreed that I am not a very skilled artist. 'No,' she added, examining my feeble effort, 'you look much older than that.'

Yet another small child I was privileged to spend time with announced to me, conspiratorially, that she was rather glad her sister had finally died as it meant a bedroom to herself for this surviving little sibling. Such forthright candour has to raise a smile, but I was struck, too, by the innate wisdom that told this child her parents would not be the suitable recipients of such information. As she *had* to tell someone, the 'death lady' (the bereavement counsellor) seemed a safe receptacle.

Conversely (and more usually), there were those occasions where the elder sibling was desperately missed. Their vacated place in the family became a harbinger of grief and the unwilling second child was keenly aware of their obligation to now be the first to encounter the milestones they had hoped to follow their elder sibling to. Moving on to secondary school could be a significantly distressing time for the bereaved sibling who had never intended to be the first in the family to attend that place (Abdelnoor and Hollins, 2004; Brown, 1999).

It is impossible to differentiate levels of poignancy within all the individual and unique situations encountered. To this day, I could not say whether the raw honesty of teenage conversations wrenched my heart the most, or the silent gaze of little ones who were too young to offer or receive any explanation of their declining health. In those circumstances, play, where appropriate, and other therapies, would have to suffice to convey a wordless empathy. I recall an occasion where a small child was drifting into his final few days. His breathing was too rapid, making him restless and agitated. The music therapist at the hospice—a gifted flautist —sat with him and improvised a melody in time with his quick breaths. As their rhythms corresponded the flute gently slowed and the little boy's breathing kept pace with it until he was breathing more naturally. I was in awe of these skills beyond medical intervention that the staff of the hospice could bring into stressful circumstances.

That same flautist accompanied me when I sang at a little girl's funeral. This child's family had wanted something unique for this final tribute to their exceptionally beautiful daughter, so I wrote a song that was uniquely hers:

Sunflower baby, some flowers may be
designed to blossom briefly,
bringing joy to all who see,
bringing sadness when they're fading,
leaving just a memory.
Too beautiful to be forgotten,
but too delicate to stay.

Sunflower baby, buttercups and daisies,
gold and silver of creation,
richest treasures we can find,
but how priceless are the memories
and the love you leave behind.
For the seeds you've sown within our hearts
will grow in strength with every day.

The family subsequently used the last two lines of the first verse as an epitaph on their daughter's gravestone. 'Too beautiful to be forgotten, but too delicate to stay' is perhaps too flowery a statement to encompass all the children and young people I have known who have died. For some of them were strapping teenagers or angry eight year olds who could swear like troopers, some had the faces of angels while others bore the ravages of their disease or treatment. But then, it is not simply their appearance that should be too beautiful to be forgotten; it is their life. Whether they lived sixteen weeks or sixteen years, from the youngest babe that I met, to the oldest of our young people, each life carried its own worth and unique contribution to our ever-spinning world. It is not an exaggeration to say that their existences have irrevocably changed mine. Within an environment where profound and multiple disability was not unusual, there were, of course, those parents whose empathetic proximity to their children gave a voice to those with no voice. Some children were unable to verbally express their thoughts or feelings, but often the parents of those children interpreted with accuracy the slightest nuance of expression. The challenge for service providers is to offer equal levels of support to those who may be inarticulate or learning disabled.

This book holds its fair share of instructive text—how to understand bereaved children; how to run a support group; how schools can help; how grief theory has changed; how…

There is, however, no instruction manual for how to value life more in the context of death. Or even how to tolerate the concept that each one of us is as vulnerable as the next, that the ultimate statistic is one in one dies, and that the saddest part of the statistics is that, still, children die—even though we might prefer that everyone reach a healthy old age and die peacefully in bed. Life is transient, and we are accustomed to seeing beauty in many transient phenomena: the fading sunset, the temporary rainbow, the fresh fall of snow, even a newborn baby's wrinkled and bemused expression. We know that none of these things will stay as they are, but we enjoy the moment—if we've taken time to notice, that is.

Children's hospice is about enjoying the moment. Children with a lot of living to do, whose families endeavour to substitute quality for quantity within the confines of the prognosis they have received. A lot of living to do indeed, but sometimes some dying to do too; and if we deny young people the opportunity to encounter, consider and prepare for their approaching death, we may be locking them into a solitary confinement that does not disappear on our denial of its existence.

References

Abdelnoor A, Hollins S (2004) ??article title?? *Educ Psychol Pract* **20**: 43–54

Bertoia J (1993) *Drawings from a Dying Child*. Routledge, London

Bluebond-Langner M (1999) Children's understanding of death. In: *Children and Death 4th International Conference*, Bristol, UK

Bluebond-Langner M (1978) *The Private Worlds of Dying Children*. Princeton University Press, Princeton

Brown E (1999) *Loss, Change and Grief*. David Fulton, London

Farrell M (1999) *Care of the Dying Child*. NT Books, London

Gibran K (1991) *The Prophet*. Macmillan, London

Herbert M (1996) *Supporting Bereaved and Dying Children and their Parents*. BPS Books, Leicester

Hodgson AK, Eden OB (2003) 'Everything has Changed'—an exploratory study of the experiences of young people with recurrent or metastitic cancer. Christie Hospital NHS Trust, Manchester

Kubler-Ross E (1983) *On Children and Death*. Macmillan, New York

Oliviere D, Monroe B (2003) *Patient Participation in Palliative Care: A Voice for the Voiceless*. Oxford University Press, London

Papadatou D (1999) The dying adolescent. In: *Children and Death 4th International Conference*, Bristol, UK

5

Family support

The role of Family Support Co-ordinator at Derian House Children's Hospice brought me into contact with dying children and every generation of their families. My appointment was the first full-time post of its type in a children's hospice, offering a unique opportunity to devise a facility that was largely informed by service-users. While individual counselling and one-to-one contact formed a large part of the remit, it was the group support programmes particularly that provoked interest from other children's hospices throughout the UK and internationally. Group interventions will be described more fully in later chapters, but I shall first expand upon the role and the illumination it offered on different grieving styles and coping mechanisms. I believe the descriptive title of my role was carefully chosen to encompass pre- and post-bereavement support for families. However, perceptions of the role varied and were reflected in the descriptions utilised by both families and colleagues. Some saw me as the bereavement counsellor, some as a befriender, others mistakenly introduced me as the 'social worker', and yet children, interestingly, often made the speedy assessment that I was the 'death lady', able to hear and contain thoughts that had often found little reception elsewhere. The families themselves came from a wide variety of backgrounds and experience. Some had known since the birth of their child of the devastating prognosis. Others had witnessed an apparently healthy child succumb to a degenerative condition, while yet others endured familial or genetic conditions that were all too well known to the family. All of these families shared the experience of child death but, nevertheless, there is a distinctiveness to each of their situations. I arrived with theoretical knowledge and some counselling experience—they arrived fully conversant, usually, with their child's condition and with an empirical knowledge of the emotional turmoil of diagnosis, prognosis and the dreadful road ahead. I was about to be educated.

The families of dying children are a notably unpredictable client group. This is both to be expected, and forgivable. Some families, on being introduced to someone they assumed to be the bereavement counsellor, would be highly reluctant to converse, their eyes conveying the understanding that I represented one more affirmation of the nightmare they were hoping still to wake from. Given that the course of their child's illness might have brought a series of fragile hopes and dashed expectations, family members could experience very erratic social responses. Some days they might need to pour out fears, anxieties—even talk about after their child dies. Other days they clung to the hope of a miracle, and a bereavement counsellor would not be an appropriate addition to that particular scenario.

The hospice at least afforded the facility for me to be informally available so that families could drop in and out of contact as it suited them. Thus my time would be divided between formal counselling sessions, more informal home visits, group activities and social settings within the hospice, such as mealtimes, where I could encounter families—or they could encounter me—in a non-threatening situation. I rapidly learnt to forge my own introductions to new families where I simply explained that I was the one who did the listening if they needed to talk. Members of the nursing team and other hospice staff were also well used to lending an empathic ear; and it is a strength within the hospice movement that many of its nurses have deliberately chosen that avenue of care because they are actively seeking the opportunity to provide holistic care. I am sure there were times when it must have appeared to hard-pressed staff that I had the better deal—with the liberty to focus continually and without distraction on families' emotional support. Members of the hospice care team were integral and vital to the support programmes instigated, and several children's hospices offer a bereavement support service that is entirely composed of nursing/care team members, perhaps on rotation. I am thankful that Derian House created, in addition to that, a full-time Family Support post, as this provided such an opportunity for development and expansion of our understanding of the families' hospice experience.

In addition to the family-centred care that was offered, the role inevitably included an administrative component, as liaison with other agencies and professionals was imperative. During the course of a child's illness, information would necessarily be continually updated and, as much of a family's contact with the hospice was for respite visits prior to terminal care, it was essential to maintain a record of both the physical and emotional journey of the family. Following the death of a child, we instituted a rather formal proceeding, the Bereavement Support Planning Meeting, which sounded like a somewhat clinical response to a very sad occasion yet provided a crucial dual function. Primarily, it offered the opportunity for a multi-agency discussion concerning the continuing needs of the bereaved family. Hence, all the practitioners who had been involved with the family would be invited to the hospice. This would include GP, consultant, community palliative care teams, teachers, social workers, occupational therapists, hospice staff and any other professionals who had supported the family. As the meeting was held as soon as possible after a child's funeral, parents were not expected to attend. They were, however, informed of the meeting and given an explanation of our need to clarify future support for them. Clearly, for some professionals, their remit ended with the death of the child, and it was helpful to know who would continue to have contact with the bereaved family and how that support role was envisioned. A key-worker would be identified who could co-ordinate bereavement support and ensure that no family was overlooked. In the vast majority of cases, the key-worker would be a member of hospice staff, usually the Family Support Co-ordinator, but on a few occasions it proved more practicable to utilise another professional. One family, who were at some geographical distance from the hospice, were supported by their local community paediatric nurses. On other occasions, where language may have proved a barrier for some ethnic minority families, social workers with the appropriate language capabilities were utilised. Some procedures carried an obvious intention to avoid unnecessary suffering for the bereaved parents. For example, it was the sincere endeavour of all professionals to ensure that families would not receive future computer-generated appointments for their deceased child, a bureaucratic error that many bereaved people can identify with. Unfortunately, some mistakes did occur, causing much grief to families, but it is hoped such oversights were limited by inter-agency communication. The Bereavement Support Planning Meeting assumed another function in that it presented an environment where professionals might express some of their own feelings around the death of a child. The sensibilities of professionals involved in caring for sick and dying children are often assumed to be controlled and detached, but it is difficult to work in that area without any emotional involvement. Indeed, it is more likely that families will appreciate that those who cared for their child also held some regard for, and were touched by, that child's existence. Those who assume that practitioners working in the field of paediatric palliative care must become hardened to child death, or remain detached, generally have misplaced assumptions. Increasingly, professionals have acknowledged the psychological strength they can restore through taking time to consider and mourn the passing of one of their young patients. The grief of parents and the wider family must always take precedence, and there can be no comparison between that grief and the sense of loss professionals might concede. Nevertheless, I believe it is the consummate professional who can dare to examine their inner thoughts and responses to loss, in order to continue, with their mental health intact, in a career that will indubitably bring a repetition of such occurrences. Marie de Hennezel, a psychologist working in a French hospice, noted this when she commented:

> 'Accompanying someone involves engaging with that person, it is a matter of the heart. Above all it is about one's common humanity. One cannot retreat behind a white coat. This does not mean that there are no limits. Everyone must remain aware of his or hers. One actually is less exhausted by a total involvement of self—provided one knows how to replenish the reserves—than by the attempt to barricade oneself behind defences. I have often seen for myself how the medical personnel who protect themselves the most are also those who complain the most about being exhausted. Those who give themselves, however, also recharge themselves at the same time.'

(De Hennezel, 1997)

Bereaved parents

Frequently, one of the prominent features of child death is the way in which the depth of sorrow and shock miraculously enables parents to function for a few days at an almost superhuman level. They often seemed imbued with an inspirational sense of pride in their child that stirred them to create and participate in a funeral service celebrating that child's contribution to the world. Onlookers and supporters are regularly amazed at, and a little envious of, the vibrant energy a bereaved parent is displaying as they fulfil this final, caring task for their child. It is, of course, one of the graces of nature that those most profoundly affected by the death will not feel the full impact for some time. I often use the analogy of accidentally slicing one's hand with a sharp blade. Knowing that we must have penetrated almost to bone, we stare in shock at this bloodless gash, waiting (the deeper the wound, the longer it takes for the blood to appear), and those few seconds send our minds into a frenzy of decision making—where are the elastoplasts? Will it need stitches? Can I drive? Am I going to faint? Should I phone someone? The surge of adrenalin can make us think speedily and remarkably rationally at times, and so, I suspect, it is with bereaved parents. How often I have attended the funeral of a child where the calmest and least tearful were the parents themselves, the lull before the storm. Again, this cannot be interpreted as a generalisation because, equally, there would be those parents who were instantly debilitated by their grief (perhaps those who had spent months in anticipatory grief). The concept of anticipatory grief suggests that parents, faced with the impending death of their child, may begin grieving in anticipation of the loss (Parkes *et al*, 1996; Worden, 1988). This may have some impact on the parents' feelings and reactions in the immediate aftermath of a child's death, but I remain unconvinced of major differences in long-term outcomes for bereaved parents. Anticipatory grief is better suited to other generational losses, in the sense that we *anticipate*, consciously or subconsciously, the deaths of our parents or grandparents. This is an inherent feature of the human life cycle and relatively easy for the mind to absorb. The death of a child, however, being the antithesis of normal human progression, is far less easy to accommodate. Some parents may have advance notice of this death and feel they have begun to grieve the anticipated loss, but I suspect that, in reality, that loss still conceals its most potent weaponry until well after the funeral. Commonly, it seemed that four, five or six months following the death would be a time when parents suffered the most agonising pains of loss. Scholars of 'tasks' or 'stages' of bereavement might recognise this as the process of accepting the reality of the loss. These are phenomena experienced by many bereaved people, not just those who have experienced the death of a child, and it is quite understandable that a trauma so profound takes some time to be absorbed by the conscious mind. For grieving parents, convinced that the worst period of grief must and should surely have been at the time of their child's death, this episode of paralysing sadness is often accompanied by confusion, guilt and self-reproach. Many times I have heard bereaved mothers say, 'I should have stopped crying by now', or 'I can't seem to pull myself together.' When their responses and feelings are normalised and assurances given that they still have permission to be devastated by their loss, the relief is palpable.

Another frequently unexpected reaction to bereavement for parents was the sheer physicality of their symptoms. The tangible pain of grief. Parents described aches and pains 'like having the flu, but not'—the sheer exhaustion of barely being able to open their eyes or think straight. Chest pains, sweating, shivering, feeling cold, headaches, sore throats and lowered immune systems ensured that parents, cruelly, were at a physical low when they least needed the additional strain. Illnesses, rashes, even recurrent outcrops of boils, were the physical manifestation of a life laid low by grief. The reduction of immune system function for a period of approximately two years following a major bereavement has been clearly acknowledged and well researched (Irwin and Pike, 1993).

This point, when bereaved families are likely to be at their lowest ebb, often heralds the arrival of friends and supporters who are convinced that some diversionary tactics are now required. The bereaved person must be distracted, kept busy, entertained and 'cheered up'. Trying to enthuse and uplift a grieving person is not only counter-productive, but it also reaffirms for the griever that they are alone, misunderstood and unwanted in their present state. On a happy occasion, a wedding perhaps, it is unlikely that guests will encourage the revellers to consider how miserable they could be if they just made the effort to do something sad... Where did the concept evolve that suggests those who are embroiled in sadness should extricate themselves by occupying themselves with 'happy' thoughts? However many textbooks we read, courses we attend, theories we endorse, the simple fact inevitably resurfaces; the death of a child is unbearably sad, most of all for the parents, and to offer any means of support that does not acknowledge that reality can be clumsy, hurtful and destructive. 'Being there', 'listening', and 'empathising' may have become counselling-speak clichés, but are nonetheless the most appropriate roles for the genuine, caring supporter to take.

Parents from the hospice were at liberty to avail themselves of counselling support at any stage and for any reason on their journey through grief, so the client-base, while having many commonalities, also carried an element of surprise and individualism that required an alert attentiveness to each unique story.

Formal counselling sessions were less frequent than the more informal home visits, but they offered an encounter of unique value that enabled individual parents to be quietly and privately circumspect in the midst of family strains and turbulent emotions. A session consisted of the 'therapeutic hour' and normally took place in my office at the hospice. As many counselling organisations beyond bereavement have discovered, family relationships can often be strengthened through members having individual encounters with psychotherapy. In bereavement, this was noticeably so, as couples within a relationship often tacitly understood their partner's inability to offer emotional support at this time, nor, indeed, did they expect or anticipate such support. The counsellor was in a prime position to be the receptacle into which they could pour the anger, fear, guilt, frustration, sorrow, without the client feeling they were burdening an already crushed partner. Of course, there would also be instances where a partner's lack of consideration or understanding would be the target of unleashed anger, but commonly this accompanied an internal wisdom where clients knew, but were reluctant to verbalise, another source to their anger.

In common with societal norms, not all parents were still in a relationship, and of the single parents, the majority were female.

Regularly, tears would be a feature of the counselling session, quite soon after arrival. I always felt this carried an almost physical manifestation of *permission*. It seemed that, even as parents stepped through the door of the office, the protective coating of the polite, proper, often quintessentially English, facade that carried them through the trivia of the day, melted away. This was the place where they could rage, fume, protest, even laugh—or simply sit with silent reflection or quiet sobs. I recall a bereaved father once sharing his sense of failure, having always been able to 'make things right' for his wife in the past. Another who confided he had loved his child more than his wife, so what was left for their relationship now? A mother consumed with guilt because her son had died from a condition passed on through the female line. Another mother whose family were unaware she returned to bed after they left in the morning and rose just before they returned. The mothers who confessed a desperate urge to return to the graveside and dig their child up; and others who endured the horror of recurrent nightmares of crematoria flames. And again and again, the insoluble predicament of maintaining an intimate relationship when each partner is too disintegrated to provide their half to the whole. Confidentiality was an essential feature of the sessions, as with all counselling, but made consistently more difficult when seeing, separately, two partners in a relationship whose greatest anxieties centred on the welfare of their partner. Boundaries had to be cautiously but explicitly established.

Home visits would more often than not be to a mother. This is not only a reflection of the proportion of single mothers, but also indicates my own reluctant compliance with the widely-held belief that mothers would need more support than fathers. That concept is perhaps the residue of a patriarchal society that anticipates emotionally vulnerable females with protective males. While I absolutely endorse, and have observed, marked gender differences in responses to grief, I would not quantify male and female support needs too rigidly. There is an assumption that men are less willing to avail themselves of some emotional support, but that, too, might be less attributable to their unwillingness and more allied to the stereotypical roles into which they are thrust. I observe that bereaved fathers are often constrained by a society that is still likely to enquire 'how is she bearing up?' thereby offering that father the relief of not having to contemplate his own tumultuous feelings and firmly closing the door on any expectation he had of being heard in his own right. It is my experience that males have an equal need for psychological support, but often less opportunity and less well-rehearsed verbalising skills in obtaining it. Certainly, women are more skilled in recognising and discussing feelings, but that is not, in itself, just cause to give bereavement support interventions a female bias. Rather, it offers the challenge of creating services that can be equally accessible to both genders, and all variations of family structure.

A notable feature of home visits was the phenomenon I termed 'door-knob syndrome', whereby my suggested departure precipitated further revelations from clients of the depth and pain of their grief. Sometimes this necessitated an extended visit, but there were also occasions when I realised the bereaved person was sowing seeds for the next encounter, experimentally airing an issue that required an interval of consideration and preparation before it could be brought to the counselling arena. This endorsed the merit of maintaining records of visits in readiness for future appointments.

A synopsis of family structure

From a random sample of 120 the many families who utilised the services of the hospice between 1996 and 2002, it is possible to gain an overview of the general structure of families.

Description	Number	%
Families	120	100.0
Single parents at time of child's illness and death	24 (2 male)	20.0
Separated since death of child	10	8.3
Death of partner since child's death	2	1.7
Couples still together	84	70.0

I endeavoured to provide home visits at weekends and evenings, as well as weekdays, to cover those couples where one partner, usually the father, might not be so readily available.

I recall a situation where a bereaved mother, devastated by her child's death, struggled for over a year with unrelenting and overwhelming symptoms of grief, which tipped over, for a period of time, into clinical depression. Her husband managed to return to work and provide the steadying presence the family required. Eighteen months later, the mother began to regain much of her emotional stability, my visiting was able to decrease and their family life regained a semblance of normality. However, within weeks, the father was suffering panic attacks, loss of appetite, sleep disturbance, listlessness and depression. The strong tower needed some scaffolding. The impact of bereavement had been great, but he had still been able to marshal his protective, supportive instincts for his family, until it was safe to reveal his own injuries. Of course, he was not consciously aware of doing that and was utterly mystified and rather frightened, when his body finally 'let him down' (an interesting phrase, 'let him down'; it could easily be a colloquialism for '*allowed him to be depressed*').

There appeared to be something inherent in the male/female roles that ensured this pattern was repeated in other couples. In other families, these anticipated roles were completely reversed, so no dogmatic principles of practice could be extrapolated, save the constant reminder of the individuality of each situation.

Other authors have written at length on gender differences and responses in bereavement (Davies, 2001; Davies *et al*, 1998; Fairbairn, 2000; Field *et al*, 1997; Rando, 1983; Rosenblatt, 2000; Rubin, 1993; Sanders, 1995), acknowledging that they are easier to observe than rationalise. There is much hypothesis regarding the cause of gender differences in ways of grieving but, having not yet researched that specific area, I can only offer the empirical knowledge gleaned from the seven years at Derian House. Rochford (Rochford, 1991), however, endorses the value of anecdotal data:

> '*Theoretical understanding of bereavement draws together the reciprocating knowledge of the normal and the abnormal*

experience, and of adult and child experience. This perspective requires us to listen not only to carefully designed research investigations, but also to the analysis of practice experience and the anecdotes of the wise. For even an anecdote, honestly told, is valid data when theory is concerned with a universal phenomenon.'

The pager system

Telephone contact was a prerequisite to the support structure for bereaved parents. Maintaining regular communication with a family was relatively easy insofar as making telephone calls from the hospice to them. Families were also at liberty to contact the Family Support Co-ordinator whenever they wished. It was soon noted that, while families were relatively easy to locate, the Family Support Co-ordinator role was rather more itinerant and constituted something of a moving target. Not only was I frequently out of the hospice on visits, but when in the hospice the phone system and movement of staff around the building often necessitated a delay for callers; distressed parents, particularly, found the anxious interval difficult or impossible to tolerate. In response to this, we instituted a pager system whereby bereaved families had a contact number, which transmitted the caller's number to a pager carried by the Family Support Co-ordinator. This guaranteed that families could be assured that their call would be promptly returned by someone who knew them and their situation. It also absolved callers of the necessity to explain their call or ask for a specific person, an onerous task when the caller was distressed. The contentious and sometimes controversial element of this system was that the pager was available to families twenty-four hours a day, seven days a week. Those within counselling, or other fields, who contend that maintaining professional boundaries includes creating designated periods of availability to clients, might recoil from such unrestricted access. Ethical considerations apart, some boundary setting must be left to individual discretion and my own concerns for families were partly allayed by the knowledge that I was accessible to them. My personal boundaries were implicit in no clients having my home telephone number, so if the pager was utilised, I knew what to expect; if my home phone rang, it would not be a bereaved parent. The offer of twenty-four hour availability of the pager number was a more speculative venture. My estimation was that bereaved parents would rarely utilise the pager at 'unsocial' hours and, fortunately, I was proved correct.

Over a six-year period 490 calls were made to the pager. Only five came in the early hours of the morning and on each of those occasions, the calls were from parents for whom I had major suicide concerns; so I could only be thankful that they had reached for the telephone and not something more destructive. In effect, the pager system functioned as a 'safety net' for bereaved families, giving them the *knowledge* of support availability without necessarily having to *employ* it excessively. In the chapter on Stepping Stones, the 'child-likeness of grief' is examined and it occurred to me that the pager number perhaps functioned as an archetypal 'transitional object' that yielded some level of intangible but viable reassurance between more concrete encounters (Winnicott, 1958). This was verbalised by bereaved parents on several occasions, one bereaved mother commenting: 'many times I've gone to pick up the phone and ring your pager, but put it back down. Sometimes just knowing you're there if I'm really desperate, is enough.'

Responding to the pager rarely precipitated an immediate visit to a bereaved parent. Predominantly, callers needed a listening ear and very little else. As time goes by in bereavement, families often feel they have exhausted the patience and understanding of friends, colleagues or even other family members, and the 'professional listener' provides the conditions of warm acceptance that allows release for all the recurring and expressive emotions of grief. Telephone counselling is an acquired skill, and if tolerating silence is an initial skill that the trainee counsellor must acquire, silence in a telephone conversation is doubly difficult to endure. Some statements from a bereaved parent warrant no response, while others lead the counsellor into simple acquiescence when there is no alternative but the disconcerting discomfort of helplessness and hopelessness. More than once, I listened to a sobbing bereaved mother saying, 'I just want him back.' What polished, considered, erudite response does a counsellor give to such a statement? All I could ever say was 'I know you do.'

There was also an open-door policy for bereaved parents whereby they were at liberty to visit the hospice and either spend time with a member of staff, or simply wander into the grounds or quiet areas, finding space for contemplation and reflection. Some families would return regularly, others less frequently but few never returned. It was another false assumption of mine that at least half the families would never want to see again the place where their child died; in actuality this was not the case. Far more families maintained contact with the hospice than did not. Return visits to the hospice tended to diminish naturally during the first two post-bereavement years, until families may have only returned for the annual Forget-me-not service. This memorial occasion is held each year in the grounds of the hospice and all bereaved families are invited. It offers an occasion for remembrance, reminiscence and the solidarity of being among other bereaved families. Staff, too, appreciate the opportunity to reflect on the core of the hospice's existence. Each family referred to the hospice has a child with a life-limiting condition and each family is ultimately (be it weeks, months or years in the future) likely to be invited to a Forget-me-not service. It is a disturbing thought and yet, on the day of the Forget-me-not service, the sight of so many families, intermittently sad but capable of *living* with their grief, has a strangely reassuring impact. The service is multicultural in intent and composed of music, readings, candle lighting and a contribution from the hospice chaplain. Regularly, some thoughts from the hospice staff would be expressed and I close this section with a composite reflection from the staff (in the year that some sapling cherry blossom trees, purchased on behalf of bereaved families, had been stolen from the driveway to the hospice).

We remember too.
Not as often as you, of course, and not as much, but we remember.

I remember the first child I met, on my first day—and now, her parents are here.
I remember a seven-year-old who could swear like a trooper and sing like an angel.

I remember a boy who made me laugh till I cried, telling me what tricks he played with his glass eye.

I remember to say poncuter instead of computer because a little girl I knew said it that way.

I remember some children I only met in the Sunflower room, and I felt the loss of not having known them better.

We remember children whose illness had changed their appearance.

And children who looked far too beautiful to die.

We remember children who clung on to life longer than anyone had thought possible.

And children who went sooner than anyone had expected.

We remember having to get more pages for the Memorial book, and more shelves in the chapel for photographs.

We remember some pain, but lots of peace.

We remember some suffering but lots of smiles.

We remember grandparents, brothers, sisters, cousins, friends…

Doctors, nurses, carers—who set out to be saviours and wound up being helpless.

We remember families who lived through being helpless and taught us how to help others.

We remember Telly Tubbies and Thomas the Tank.

Postman Pat and Fireman Sam.

Football clubs, pop stars and pets—who all visited to remind us they cared.

We remember songs and poems,

Sunflowers and Forget-me-nots,

We remember cherry trees, stolen from us to blossom somewhere we do not know and cannot see—

But they will blossom.

Most of all we remember children, and the privilege of being saddened by their deaths but enriched by their lives.

We remember them all,

And we remember you,

And we thank you for sharing your children, your memories, and days like this, with us.

References

Davies AM (2001) Death of adolescents: parental grief and coping strategies. *Br J Nurs* **10**: 13–24

Davies B, Deveau E, deVeber B, *et al* (1998) Experiences of mothers in five countries whose child died of cancer. *Cancer Nurs* **21**: 301–11

De Hennezel M (1997) *Intimate Death*. Warner Books, London

Fairbairn G (2000) When a baby dies—a father's view. In: Dickenson D, Johnson M, Katz JS, eds. *Death, Dying and Bereavement*. Sage, London

Field D, Hockey J, Small N (1997) *Death, Gender and Ethnicity*. Routledge, London

Irwin M, Pike J (1993) Bereavement, depressive symptoms and immune function. In: Stroebe M, Stroebe W, Hansson RO, eds. *Handbook of Bereavement Theory, Research and Intervention*. University of Cambridge Press, Cambridge

Parkes CM, Relf M, Couldrick A (1996) *Counselling in Terminal Care and Bereavement*. BPS Books, Leicester

Rando TA (1983) An investigation of grief and adaptation in parents whose children have died from cancer. *J Paediatr Psychology* **8**: 3–20

Rochford G (1991) Theory, concepts, feelings and practice: The contemplation of bereavement within a social work course. In: Lishman J, ed. *Handbook of Theory for Practice Teachers in Social Work*. Jessica Kingsley, London

Rosenblatt PC (2000) *Parent Grief: Narratives of Loss and Relationship*. Brunner/Mazel, Philadelphia

Rubin SS (1993) The death of a child. In: Stroebe M, Stroebe W, Hansson RO, eds. *Handbook of Bereavement*. Cambridge University Press, New York

Sanders CM (1995) Grief of children and parents. In: Doka KJe, ed. *Children Mourning, Mourning Children*. Taylor and Francis, Bristol, USA

Winnicott DW (1958) *Collected Papers: Through Paediatrics to Psycho-analysis.* Hogarth Press, London

Worden JW (1988) *Grief Counselling and Grief Therapy.* Routledge, London

6

Stepping Stones: A bereavement support programme for parents

The Stepping Stones bereavement support programme was initiated in 1997 following a year of assimilating needs and experiences of bereaved parents. A questionnaire was distributed seeking guidance from earlier bereaved families who graciously described what they felt *they would* have found helpful had there been a group programme available at the time of their bereavement. From this, we were able to recognise choices around venue, timing, group structure, childcare arrangements and content. This assistance from bereaved parents, who were not themselves to benefit from the new programme, was invaluable and we were enormously grateful for their unselfishly generous contribution.

Choice of venue was an element that particularly surprised me; initial suggestions of holding the meetings at alternative venues, such as a local hall, a pub, or someone's home, quickly gave way to the overwhelming majority, who felt the sessions should take place at the hospice, which, indeed, they subsequently did. Respondents also advocated joint groups, as opposed to gender split groups, and stressed the need for childcare arrangements for surviving siblings of the deceased child who were too young to remain at home alone.

What began as a childcare facility rapidly evolved into a semi-structured group running concurrently with Stepping Stones and imaginatively titled, by the play specialist who co-ordinated it, as *Pebbles*. This group consisted, naturally, of bereaved siblings who had their own needs and welcomed the opportunity of spending time with other bereaved youngsters, while their parents attended Stepping Stones. Pebbles incorporated a mixture of free-play sessions, memorialisation, art and craft work, reminiscence and loquacious suppertimes when children chatted freely about their lives and the loss of their sibling. It was an inspirational innovation for which I can take no credit, but which reflected the informed enthusiasm of other hospice staff who readily saw a need and rallied around to meet it.

The final constitution of Stepping Stones:

- To offer a nine-month programme of group support to bereaved parents

- To be offered to parents who were between four and eight months post-bereavement

- It would take place once a month for two hours, in an evening, at the hospice

- Each programme would be led by the same two members of staff (initially the Family Support Co-ordinator and a member of the care team)

- It would be of a semi-structured design to offer some educative content, as well as informal times for sharing

- Each group would be a closed group for the duration of the programme and a rolling programme would evolve with a new group commencing every six months to accommodate future bereaved parents

- No group would exceed twenty parents.

Much of the structure had evolved in response to the questionnaire results, but some features were in response to practitioner experiential evidence from counselling bereaved parents. It was felt that parents should be aware of the duration of the programme from the outset, as I was aware of the difficulty some participants experience in knowing when to cease attending a group for bereaved parents. This knowledge could give parents a sense of control over their commitment and also a sense of achievement as months passed and the 'end' was in sight. Ongoing individual contact and counselling support for families was available and did not necessarily end with the conclusion of Stepping Stones, but there was generally a diminishing of support needs by the end of the programme.

The timing of parents' invitations to Stepping Stones was ascertained through the awareness that the very earliest months of bereavement were not appropriate for the emotional and psychological demands of a group support programme. Also, the timing of commencement and the length of the programme ensured that parents usually passed the first anniversary of their child's death while participating in Stepping Stones. Anniversaries are notoriously poignant times and the solidarity of being around other parents at similar stages was considered to be beneficial.

Conducting the group in an evening clearly facilitated the attendance of many of the working parents, although on occasion shift work proved a disruption for some. Locating the group at the hospice was probably the most controversial decision, but endorsed by our questionnaire respondents. Certainly, for families who had rarely or never returned since the death of their child, simply arriving and entering on the first evening was an achievement. However, it transpired that, despite its associations, families also welcomed the familiarity of the hospice environment. Sessions were held in the lounge, a room well known to most families from earlier times.

We were determined to offer an informative and educative structure to the sessions, as many parents had expressed their discomfort with other groups they had encountered where tea and coffee but little else was provided, and participants squirmed uncomfortably, as (usually) one dominant character fully occupied the gathering with their story. While I must acknowledge some degree of control on my part (a barely acknowledged desire to see the group take my pre-determined route), I also felt that information and knowledge empower grievers and can lessen the power imbalance between them and 'experts' with theoretical and professional learning. Incidentally, there were occasions when the group did not follow my 'pre-determined route' and I was forced to reassess and implement my belief in participant ownership of the group.

The decision to offer each programme as a closed group was not difficult. It was transparently clear that the sensitivity of the topic would merit trust and confidence in group members. This would be damaged by the introduction of new members at intervals during the programme, so the idea of rolling programmes of nine-month duration was easily adopted. While a maximum of twenty participants had been set, groups rarely came close to that figure. The largest group consisted of seventeen members, with several other groups numbering in the teens, and the smallest was reduced to five after two families ceased attending. Naturally, the number of invitees was governed by the number of bereavements in the previous six months. All families were offered Stepping Stones and the up-take was approximately 50 per cent of bereaved families. Reasons offered for not accepting the invitation ranged from 'can't make that time' to 'I'm not good with groups' or 'what good will it do' and 'I don't want to talk about it'. A research project waiting to be undertaken, I am sure, but one that has not yet been established. Rowa-Dewar (2002) conducted a systematic review of interventions for bereaved parents and, although she felt the review results suggested, overall, no beneficial effect of bereavement support programmes, her conclusion was: *'Parental grief interventions that target a wide range of psychological, social and practical issues in mourning can be effective in reducing psychological symptoms and marital dysfunction in highly distressed parents.'* However, the Stepping Stones programme was not part of that review and we can only offer the subjective data compiled from a series of Stepping Stones programmes.

Out of the 120 random sample families mentioned earlier, 64 (120 parents) opted to join a Stepping Stones programme.

Participants in Stepping Stones	Number	%
Couples	56	87.50
Single parents	8 female	12.50
Couples where only one partner attended	4 female 1 male	6.25 1.56
Did not complete	7 couples 1 single mother	10.94 1.56

A description of the group was composed that seemed sufficiently informative but not too overwhelming, in order to give parents some foreknowledge of the programme as they made their choice. Parents were formally invited to join the Stepping

Stones programme at the designated time and were asked to return a response slip. This made it relatively painless to decline, as well as giving staff advance details of anticipated numbers. After the initial group, awareness of the programme tended to permeate the hospice language and subsequent families were often aware of the programme long before their invitation to it.

A notable feature of the Stepping Stones programme was the high attendance levels by bereaved fathers. Bereavement interventions and bereavement support services are predominantly accessed more by women than men (Clare, 2000; Davies, 2001; Doka, 1995; Field *et al*, 1997; Klass, 1999). Of the sixty-four sample families indicated above, eight were single parents; seven couples withdrew; four married mothers attended without their partner, leaving ninety-five attendees, forty-eight of whom were male. This is an unusual attendance rate but, without further research, can only be hypothetically evaluated. Nevertheless, my hypothesis would be that prior relationship with the group facilitators was paramount to acceptance of the support programme. Because these were families who were already known to the facilitator, and likely to be in receipt of individual or family support, they had opportunity to enquire about the Stepping Stones programme, express some of their anxieties or concerns and receive verbal feedback on the content of the course. Deliberately making home visits at a time when both parents could be present was, I am sure, a decisive factor in couples attending Stepping Stones together. Once the pattern had been set, it was clear that men were encouraged and enlightened through their encounters with other bereaved fathers, and, anecdotally, endorsement spread indicating the programme was particularly suited to both parents.

Stepping Stones sessions

Session one

Once families had taken the daunting step across the threshold of Derian House again, children were introduced to their session and parents were ushered into the lounge and rewarded with some refreshments—at the suggestion of parents, wine was added to the choices and was often preferred by the non-drivers over tea, coffee or fruit-juice. It must be acknowledged that every 'first night' of a group carried an atmosphere of foreboding that was almost tangible. Despite reassurances by letter and in conversation, parents inevitably arrived with the fear that they might be asked to do something they could not countenance; like stand before a group of strangers and talk about their child who had died. No amount of denial on my part seemed to allay this fear until the first session was over and parents had experienced the mindset of the group.

The session began with an explanation of how Stepping Stones had been formulated, describing the closed group design and the information received from previously bereaved parents. Parents were congratulated on making it to the first session and reminded that they would have only eight more to go—the importance of being able to see the end from the beginning. Each attendee was given a folder with some initial information, to which they could add the various handouts or pieces of 'homework' that arose during the course of the programme.

Although compiling a group contract would be an important feature later in the session, two 'rules' were stressed at the outset.

a) Try to become comfortable with discomfort. Tears will be almost inevitable at times, but if participants really felt the need to leave the room and take some time out, an adjoining room was available for that purpose;

b) No comparing. In the inevitable exchange of stories, or prior knowledge of each other, it would be all too easy to 'compare' losses—is loss of a baby easier than loss of an adolescent? Is it harder for a single parent? Is loss of an only child the worst of all? And so on. Each loss is unique to that particular family and none of it bears comparison.

Secondly, we introduced 'tree-blobs': an illustration of various figures on and around tree branches that illustrated perhaps isolation, partnership, satisfaction, triumph, supporting another, falling, waving, flat on the ground, and various other postures that could relate to feelings. It was stressed that this was not a competition (interestingly, male participants often presumed the intention was to 'reach the top of the tree'), but simply a quirky checking-in mechanism that each month would start with, to give individuals an opportunity to reflect on how they felt at that specific moment (given that they were also highly likely to run the entire gamut of emotions in the course of just one day). Participants were always entitled to pass and not share their feelings if preferred.

Focusing on the tension in the room, we then compiled a flip-chart page of fears and expectations for the sessions. After a hesitant start, fears proved more easy to locate than expectations. Examples of their fears included:

'Having to talk'
'Revealing things to partner'
'Feeling silly if upset'
'Silence'
'Finding own feelings'
'Losing temper'
'Showing feelings in a group'

Expectations were more difficult to identify, reflecting perhaps the supreme effort families had made in accepting the invitation to the group and acknowledging their primarily negative mindset of bereavement. However, some hopes and expectations eventually materialised, offering the following examples:

'Finding people who understand'
'To feel better'
'Understanding why I feel how I feel'
'Talking about my child'
'Learning about grief'

Belatedly, we then allowed the group to introduce themselves, giving only their first name and the town where they lived. This offered the opportunity for even the most reticent member to say something simple and non-threatening, as well as beginning to create group cohesion.

Following this, we established a ritual that would be repeated in the first few sessions. In order to memorise some names, it is often effective to associate the practice with an activity and we deliberately instituted a particularly frivolous one. A large, stuffed toy—a pig—was thrown between group members as they called out the name of the recipient. Errors of names contributed to the general hilarity, but names were also speedily assimilated in the process. Apart from learning each other's names during Pass-the-Pig, as the ritual became known, it also marked the point at which group members began to relax. The change in atmosphere was tangible as members realised this was not going to be an entirely sombre and earnest programme. In keeping with Stroebe's Dual-Process model of grief (Stroebe and Schut, 1995), it was essential for parents to experience some light relief amid the strenuous psychotherapeutic labour of the sessions. Having broken the ice, we would take a refreshment break halfway through the proceedings and parents were free to chat with one another or take some time apart as they wished.

Following the break, we set to and constructed the ubiquitous group contract for the programme. While constructed independently by each subsequent group, this inevitably included;

- Confidentiality
- Respect
- No comparing
- Punctuality (or notification of lateness/non-attendance)
- Time-out
- Permission for laughter and tears
- Preferable, but non-compulsory, participation.

The group were also offered the, non-compulsory, suggestion of homework. This took the form of, say, keeping a journal of their experiences through the programme for their own perusal only. Additionally, we suggested they contemplate two activities they could *begin* to do. Starting something, as opposed to giving up something, was stressed as this carries a much more positive philosophy. Suggestions like walking more, replacing every other cup of coffee with a glass of water, eating a proper breakfast and so on were presented.

The first session concluded with some 'Health Warnings'. It is normal to feel a surge of emotional pain after commencing a group such as this. Parents were advised to try not to feel too discouraged if they found themselves feeling a little more fragile than usual in the days ahead. The analogy given to explain this phenomenon was that of 'packing the wound'. A deep physical wound sometimes necessitates packing in order to prevent it scabbing over superficially and allowing unseen abscesses to form, giving rise to infection and the need for drainage. With deep emotional wounds, grievers are often encouraged (in Western society) to 'scab over' superficially and keep up a public facade. Therefore, joining a group such as Stepping Stones might feel rather like ripping off the dressing, and it is natural for participants to feel somewhat raw and exposed. Painful though that is, the hope of the months ahead would be to pack that emotional wound and encourage parents to heal from the inside out, more healthily. Given their awareness of this possible response, parents were encouraged to be kind and forgiving of themselves in their vulnerability. The accessibility of support staff was also reiterated for those who might feel the need to examine their response to the first session.

Ultimately, parents were counselled to try and not leave the place with more grief than they had arrived with. A timely quotation from the work of Rochford suggests 'Other people's grief will make you sad, but remember it is their grief and your sadness' (Rochford, 1991). Each participant has enough grief of their own and cannot spare the emotional fuel to carry someone else's as well. A date for the next session is set and a group of relieved parents exit, knowing that at least arriving for subsequent sessions should never be as difficult again.

Session two

It was apparent that parents would arrive at the second session with less fears and more assurance of what to expect. This meant that less time needed to be allowed for introductions, explanations and allaying fears, so subsequent sessions tended to have a greater proportion of group interaction and challenging content. The second session started with a repetition of tree-blobs as a check-in mechanism and a quick round of Pass-the-Pig to remind members of each other's names. Printed versions of the group contract would be distributed and reviewed.

We then went on to some more demanding exercises as we examined grief in more detail and the group compiled a flip-chart of 'feelings'. These were, however, separated into the 'obvious' feelings and the 'surprising'—or socially unacceptable—feelings. Parents rapidly understood and identified with the concept that some of their feelings could be legitimately shared with friends and family who were unsurprised at grievers' expressions of sadness, lethargy, frustration, sleeplessness... but parents found it harder to express, and have understood, their feelings of anger, guilt, isolation. Some feelings were acknowledged that surprised the parents themselves, such as the unexpectedly physical sensations of grief or the terrifying fear that they were going insane. Remarkably for only their second group session, parents shared quite revealingly and were clearly relieved to find others who could identify with their hitherto private concerns.

Some input from the group facilitator followed, introducing the precept that *avoidance depletes energy*. This became a byword of the sessions, as we explained how when we try to avoid issues, this can often consistently leach away our attention and energy. For example, **dieting**: people become consumed with thoughts about food. Or the irrepressible desire to laugh in a solemn situation. It is a quirk of human nature that we are drawn to think about whatever we are trying to avoid, hence the proverbial Freudian slip. Similarly, in grief, while the bereaved are often induced to 'keep busy' and 'take their mind off it', the paradox is that *leaning into the pain* (Humphrey and Zimpfer, 1996) can bring relief and renewed energy. Griefwork is hard work and one needs purposeful breaks. However, not to grieve or experience the pain is to deny the healing process and perhaps complicate it. Therefore, the more parents tell themselves not to be upset, to be strong, to 'cope', the more their feelings will be desperate to find expression. *'What cannot be acknowledged will be behaviourally acted out'* (Kuykendall, 1998), and parents will feel out of control and bewildered.

Following an interval for refreshments, the group returns to their flip-chart of feelings and examines the coping mechanisms they utilise when specific feelings overwhelm. It is stressed that coping mechanisms can be very individual rather than universal. What helps one griever may be anathema to another. Nevertheless, an assortment of ideas and thoughts are shared amid a curious mixture of sombre reflection and self-conscious hilarity.

Some of the suggested coping mechanisms:

- 'go to bed'
- 'clean the house'
- 'smash something'
- 'joking'
- 'shouting'
- 'drive fast'
- 'exercise'
- 'time alone'
- 'music'
- 'sex'.

This latter coping mechanism induced a challenging discussion whereby it transpired that the male members of the group found the intimacy of sex comforting and reassuring. Conversely, the female members of the group were at pains to understand their partner's need for intimacy, as the 'enjoyment' of a sexual encounter seemed almost a betrayal in the middle of their abiding grief. Within the comparative safety of a group of like-minded people, couples were enabled to unpack this sensitive issue with a frankness and rationality that was probably lacking during their more private discussions. Both male and female members of the group experienced camaraderie with their peers, but were also enabled to consider sympathetically the feelings of their partner. It was a breakthrough moment, often repeated in subsequent groups and the staff facilitating found it hard to conceive that this group were only meeting for the second time.

Gender differences were examined on a wider scale, with increasing understanding of self and others becoming apparent.

The session moves on to examine loss history. It is a fallacy that one becomes 'hardened' to loss. In fact, the effect of loss can be cumulative (Kubler-Ross, 1970) and the group is encouraged to reflect on its own loss history, incorporating a variety of events that Elizabeth Kubler-Ross termed 'the little deaths of life', such as house moves, job changes, divorce, surgery, redundancy, other bereavements. Adaptation to all these will influence the ways in which someone grieves the loss of a child, although nothing will have compared or prepared for this, the most painful of losses.

At the conclusion of this session, parents are introduced to a simplified version of Bowlby's Attachment Theory (Bowlby, 1969). His work on separation and attachment drew conclusions that are initially mystifying to many bereaved parents, but ultimately find a place in their understanding. Bowlby concluded that 'the ability to tolerate separation (anxiety) is a sign of deep attachment'. Ultimately, the loss of a warm and loving relationship can be grieved more healthily than the loss of an ambivalent relationship. Parents often expressed confusion over this statement assuring me that 'the more you love, the more you hurt'. However, Bowlby's conclusions do not suggest pain-free grieving, rather they predict healthy grieving, uncomplicated by regrets, guilt or secret histories.

Session three

In the third session, following the checking-in process, the group focused on anniversaries and places; those dates on the calendar that blazed their significance, and those places that were either difficult or comforting to revisit.

A poem, '*The Elephant in the Room,*' is shared, written by a widowed husband expressing his frustration that visitors seem determined to speak of anything else but his deceased wife. Parents recognise this scenario, too, and share occasions where stilted conversations have cautiously edged around the observable grief.

Revising the concept of avoidance depleting energy, we note that anniversaries have two elements: they cannot be eradicated from the calendar; they can, however, be anticipated and planned for. There are very obvious anniversaries, like a child's birthday, the date of their death, Christmas, and so on. However, parents identify many other occasions that loom large on the calendar: the date of diagnosis, the date of the funeral, school terms, Mother's Day and Father's Day, other family members' birthdays; any occasion, really, where the gathering of family or friends is marked by a noticeable and poignant absence. As indicated earlier, it is likely that parents will, while attending Stepping Stones, pass the first anniversary of their child's death. Much mutual support is evidenced as parents become aware of other group members' 'special' dates: encouragement is given, cards are exchanged and absences forgiven.

As for places, parents highlighted venues that carried their own memories, some sweetly comforting and others saturated with painful memory triggers. Comparisons were made between the most difficult places to be and other environments that brought consolation and warm reflection.

Discussion evolved around 'coping', that oft-abused term that has become associated, in the vocabulary of grief, with overcoming, concealing or denying. Parents berate themselves that they are not 'coping' if they are crying too much (by their own assessment), or experiencing any other symptoms of grief when they feel they should be 'coping better by now'. I recall once asking Jim Kuykendall, an American psychotherapist, for his psychological definition of 'coping'. He promptly responded that *'coping is an adaptive response to the stimuli in the present'*. To my bemused look, he translated, *'It means if you're sad you cry, and when you're happy, you laugh.'* This very logical interpretation of the dreaded word brought understanding, integrated with permission, to parents. Grieving is a normal process; every psychologist since Freud has concurred with that, and the erratic feelings associated with it will incur their differing responses, but each one appropriately located is a form of coping.

Following the refreshment break, the session continued with an overview of cognitive behavioural therapy and the understandings of affective, cognitive and behavioural responses that can impact upon the way a griever thinks and behaves. Having identified times and places that constitute affective triggers for grieving parents, responses can be scrutinised, planned for and even, in some instances, forestalled. Parents are prompted to consider how they might approach future anniversaries or daunting occasions. Christmas, for example; will they celebrate in their customary family style, or will they introduce changes? Will it be more tolerable to go away for Christmas, or preferable to maintain familiar rituals? The discussion inevitably turned to gifts and cards. Some parents acceded to the overwhelming urge to buy a gift in the name of their child who had died, either keeping it unopened, or donating it to a charity. Many found it impossible to write Christmas cards excluding the name of their deceased child, and various solutions were mooted. Some simply sent no cards; others still included their deceased child's name while other families compromised by using a symbol—a star, or a butterfly—in place of the child's name. No one can dictate a right or wrong procedure in these areas of great uncertainty and discomfort. Families found their own route through, although my especial favourite was the concept of signing family cards from 'Jane, John, Claire and Michael... and not forgetting Sarah'. A good compromise, I felt, between inclusion and acknowledgement.

Session four

The fourth session adopted the customary checking-in mechanism, which parents were now becoming somewhat blasé about, arriving with pre-prepared responses for the blobs on the tree. Laughter was an increasing feature of sessions that particularly endorsed our decision to create closed groups. The ability to relax and share laughter, as well as the more compassionate moments that arose, was testimony to the security and confidence that had developed. While laughter is an essential ingredient of normal healthy living, bereaved families often voiced the concern that it was deemed unseemly to be observed laughing, or even smiling, in public. However, with a group of companionable, like-minded contemporaries such constraints were lifted and, paradoxically, the bereaved parents' group became one of the most relaxed and forgiving environments in which they found themselves.

The serious business of the session was to look at dimensions of loss: the spirals and weavings that constituted a much wider impact of bereavement than the casual onlooker might consider. Many people, who may know someone that has lost a child, will be sympathetic to the agony of such a loss; they may even reflect on how awful it would be to lose one of their own children, and they will send condolences and anticipate a profound period of grieving for the bereaved parents. However, few will be fully cognisant of the wider implications of that loss, and bereaved parents themselves may only gradually become aware of other ramifications of the death of their child.

So, interspersed with the usual refreshment break, this session examines the following dimensions of loss; the framework was adapted from the unpublished work of Susan le Poidevin (Parkes *et al*, 1996):

- *Identity*: has loss changed how parents view themselves? Often they might have been identified through their sick child. One mother explained that, for ease of recognition and speed of service, she always identified herself as 'Paula's mother' whenever she phoned her GP practice. And inevitably, the tragic query of parents who had lost their only child—'Am I still a mother? Am I still a father?' (yes, and yes!)

- *Physical*: the stress-related symptoms of grief. Bereaved parents may feel physically impaired; exhaustion, lack of concentration, and disturbed sleep. Parents commonly experienced weight changes, either through lack of appetite or, conversely, through comfort eating. Minor illnesses were also common, attributable to the lowered immune system function evidenced in the bereaved (Irwin and Pike, 1993)

- *Emotional*: an emotional response to bereavement is without doubt expected, but there are anomalies. Unresponsive or unpredictable emotions can confuse parents and undermine their already lowered confidence. Radical changes in their usual persona can occur. Previously garrulous and outgoing personalities may become introspective and withdrawn. Equally, those who were once reticent about airing their feelings may find a voice and become someone whose heart is prominently displayed on their sleeve

- *Family/community*: are they helpful or unhelpful? A tragedy can reveal the cracks in relationships as well as the strengths. Not all extended families are sympathetic and supportive. Nor can local communities always be relied upon for support and understanding. Are families embraced or shunned by their community (and which would they prefer)? Schools may be wonderfully supportive, yet some schools may show little compassion for a family's situation or the unusual behaviour of bereaved siblings

- *Lifestyle*: has the family been financially disadvantaged? Frequently, at least one parent's career will have been put on hold, sometimes both. Homes may have been adapted to accommodate a sick or disabled child. Where families were in receipt of DLA (Disability Living Allowance) to care for their child, it will have halted promptly with no substitute income unless a parent returns swiftly to paid employment

- *Practical*: can parents manage their changed lifestyle? Some children may have had a condition that merited the support of a Mobility Allowance car , which would have to be returned, radically affecting the family's transport options. If parents do wish to return to employment, what are the childcare considerations for surviving children? This might not have been an issue previously if a parent was constantly available to see to the needs of a sick child. Is there a loss of direction—and too much available time?

- *Spiritual*: has a close encounter with death challenged their core spiritual beliefs? If parents had a religious faith prior to their child's death, has it been shaken or strengthened—or remained steady? For those who had no overt faith, has there been a change? What feelings are there around life and death? Where do parents seek for meaning, hope, and peace?

This is a challenging and intense session that provokes much discussion. A question posed by a parent in one group revealed that, although the group was composed of a mixture of nominal Christians, practising Christians, a Muslim family, some atheists and several agnostics, each participant conceded that they believed their child had 'gone somewhere'. This concurs with narratives with other bereaved parents (Rosenblatt, 2000). It seems appropriate to close this session with the words of Khalil Gibran in *The Prophet*:

> '*Your joy is your sorrow unmasked*
> *And that selfsame well from which your laughter rises*
> *was oftentimes filled with your tears.*'

Session five

This session was originally designed to examine the needs of bereaved children. After some consideration of parents who may have no surviving children, we concluded that most parents nonetheless had contact with children—wider family and friends—who may have been affected by the death of their child. Therefore the topic, while perhaps more relevant to some parents than others, still seemed an appropriate choice to include. Children's cognitive development in relation to understanding of death is related in more detail in the chapter on *Bereaved Children*, but in this Stepping Stones session we briefly covered:

- *Babyhood*: Babies may not be overwhelmingly affected by a death in the family, but they will sense something is wrong. Loss of a primary carer would have the greatest impact, which is not the area encountered by a children's hospice. Bowlby's (1969) observations of babies' responses to loss through protesting, withdrawing and despairing are reiterated

- *3–6 year-olds* (approximately): children at this stage believe the world revolves around them (egocentric), which can have the adverse effect of them assuming all events, including bad and sad ones, must have been influenced by them. In some situations, small children can feel they are to blame for a death, especially if they had ambivalent feelings towards the one who died. Children are often too young to understand the concept of 'foreverness' at this stage. They may know all the facts of a situation, but not necessarily be able to relate to them

- *7–11 year olds* (approximately): this is the period when children grasp the concept of death and finality. Sadly, it might be quite a difficult and unsettling time to encounter the death of a sibling, as this brings the surviving youngsters into stark confrontation with their own mortality. This is not normally considered until much later in development, so brings a premature awareness of the fragility of life which may result in some regressive behaviour. It is important to think of such reactions as a normal response to an abnormal situation

- *Adolescence*: adolescence is a time of loss and change, even without bereavement being added to the catalogue of tumultuous emotions. Teenagers can be notoriously uncommunicative, so it may be difficult for them to find an outlet for all their feelings. Music, sport and aggressive behaviour are common outlets.

Honesty and permission are the bywords for relating to youngsters. Honest responses to questions, honest acceptance of all their feelings and permission for youngsters to be however they are. All children learn by example, and the more they discover how the adults around them can be upset, weary, tearful, busy—as well as at times more buoyant—the more it normalises children's own confused feelings.

The material of this session expanded, however, beyond expectation because parents, while learning some of the fundamentals of child development, were also considering themselves and their own inner child. Parents rapidly appreciated the obvious similarities between some of their own feelings and those of a child. The session evolved into an unplanned discussion on the child-likeness of grief—a consideration that has since exercised my mind to an even greater extent. Parents noted, and verbalised, how much of adult grief could correlate with child-like precepts rooted within the adult. Concepts such as the magical thinking of the three-year-old, the questioning of later years, the mood swings of the adolescent, could very easily transfer to those feelings and responses associated with early grief in adults. In a brain-storming session, bereaved parents themselves recorded the following symptomatic feelings of grief as being particularly child-like:

Even those unutterable thoughts about wishing it had been someone else's child were alluded to.

Encapsulated within this child-like dynamic are the mood swings culminating in tears or laughter. These two extremes of emotion, such prominent and alternating facets of early childhood, are usually honed to a much narrower spectrum in adulthood. As we grow, our inhibitions grow with us, although we prefer to term it *self-control*. The trauma of grief tends to undermine our self-control and bereaved parents find themselves once more at the mercy of unharnessed mood swings. Tears and sadness are an obvious and understandable element of grief and distress, but also an expression of love. A major difficulty for bereaved adults in our society is the embarrassment tears can elicit. Bereaved parents who can allow themselves their tears, as a token of love for a lost child, are more likely to accept their grief in an emotionally healthy manner (Lendrum and Syme, 1992).

If grief reflects so much of our inner child, it is hardly surprising that storytelling should constitute part of the reparative nature of griefwork, resulting in the recent endorsement of narrative approaches with bereaved parents.

It is emphasised that child*like* is not to be confused with child*ish*. The intention is never to disparage any adult coping mechanisms, but to encourage grievers towards an insight into their own growth and development. Just as practical skills learned in childhood are spontaneously integrated into our maturing self, so the emotional repertoire for dealing with adversity must take root along our developmental journey. A return to basic instincts when under threat is an acceptable survival technique. Adults have been seduced by societal pressures into being all too often ashamed of their more childlike responses in grief, whereas they could be encouraged to respect their inner, disarmingly honest, child who may have lain dormant for years until such a time as this.

During the refreshment break a number of children's books relating to grief are available for parents to peruse. Often these simple stories and analogous interpretations of death can have meaning for adults too, and offer useful opportunities for restorative family sharing and togetherness. The books include: Stickney's *Waterbugs and Dragonflies*; Gliori's *No Matter What*; and Ironside's *Huge Bag of Worries* (all included among others in the Appendix).

As with several other sessions, parents are given a handout to take home, covering some of the detail of the session, and also an article suggesting ways in which adult leisure and relaxation activities might relate to earlier childhood pastimes; i.e. plasticine play becomes pottery, organising and sorting games become 'tidying the sock drawer'—a light-hearted look at our need to revisit some of the activities of our childhood in order to attend to our holistic needs.

Session six

Expanding upon the closing theme of the last session—holistic care—this session is founded on self-care. This is probably the hardest message to promote with bereaved parents as they regularly consider any form of self-care as self-indulgent, self-centred, self-absorbed and selfish. Their natural inclination is often more inclined towards self-neglect as a subtle 'punishment' for no longer being able to care for a dying child. The directive I often pronounced, that my bereaved clients should 'be kind to themselves', I knew regularly fell on deaf ears.

However, we persisted in explaining the merits of self-care, if only because caring for oneself at least equips one to support others in the family, too.

The tools utilised to frame the session are:

- Sanctuary
- Rituals
- Symbols
- Relaxation.

Sanctuary

In considering sanctuary, the group reflect on a place where it is beneficial for them to spend time. This might be a certain room; a favourite chair; an area of the garden; even a graveside or cemetery—or even a much-loved poem or book that lifts the spirits. The concept of a place with a feel-good factor is relatively alien to many bereaved parents, and it often takes some gentle probing to assist their understanding of a place of peace and calm, not necessarily a place of exuberant joy.

Rituals

Rituals focus on many of the incidental habits of our daily living which are so absorbed into daily life that we do not even realise they have become rituals. The human mind and body like repetition; it is what strengthens our neurological pathways and muscular-skeletal frameworks from earliest days, so we are often creatures of habit. Unfortunately, many habits abruptly cease through the death of a child, so it is important for those rituals that can be to be maintained to the benefit of a griever's mental and physical health.

Some of the rituals for consideration include:

- *Bedtime*: suggestions of milky drinks; stretching, curling and unwinding exercises (how often do people sleep in the foetal position?) Reading a choice of literature that is conducive to restful sleep

- *Bathtime*: is time taken to luxuriate or is this another self-indulgence that has been banned by the 'punitive super-ego' (Jacobs, 2002), perhaps better known as 'conscience'? Bathtime suggestions include, unsurprisingly, music, candles, massage, oils, skincare…

- *Work end/mood change*: what rituals mark the end of the working day, whether that is a return from the workplace or simply a change into the more relaxed atmosphere of the evening? All sorts of rituals emerge—from changing clothes, taking a shower, putting on slippers, taking a nap, to walking the dog or switching on the TV. Rituals often convey messages to our body that indicate the comfort of a familiar routine is being rehearsed

- *Tea-making ceremony*: a whimsical challenge to parents (their 'homework' for this session) to watch a kettle boil. Contrary to the proverbial dictum that 'a watched pot never boils', a supervised kettle does, in fact, boil just as quickly as an unwatched one. It is, however, an allegory of our hurried and overflowing lifestyle that a kettle is invariably switched on to make a cup of tea and another task is undertaken—filling the washing machine, unloading the dishwasher—while the kettle boils. Bereaved parents, especially, are disinclined to spend two contemplative minutes doing nothing for fear of where their thoughts might take them. Remembering session two's directive that 'avoidance depletes energy', parents are challenged to take time watching the pot boil and allow themselves a couple of minutes of reflection.

After the break for refreshments, the session continues with symbols.

Symbols

'Symbols' refers to those items that people possess that carry an associated meaning, preferably ones that carry such vivid memories they induce a smile, even a tearful one. Symbolism is not unfamiliar to parents—bereaved or not—as we recall the souvenirs and treasures of a child's life stored in various places about the home. The lock of hair? The first shoes? The baby clothes? The school photos? Familiar paraphernalia to many a family. Other symbols remind us of holidays well spent, or achievements gained. One of my own examples is a stone retrieved from the top of a French mountain when I conquered (or tolerated!) my fear of cable cars in order to accompany my family to the most beautiful and exhilarating scenery I had ever experienced. With prompting, parents realised they had many such symbols cataloguing the highs and lows of their family life, and, of course, many that related directly to their child who had died. The intention of the session is to endorse the value of these symbols, to treasure their meaning and allow ourselves the indulgence of retrospection to strengthen us also for the ongoing journey of life. There are appropriate moments in group or individual therapeutic work for strategic self-disclosure on the part of the facilitator. This session proved to be one such occasion. As well as the tale of the cable car, I shared with parents how I particularly relish the month of May, when the English countryside is dotted with bright yellow as the rapeseed fields flower. No matter what frame of mind I might be in, I am forced to smile when a car journey suddenly amazes me with a bright blaze of yellow. Years later, a bereaved mother wrote to me, including in her letter the assertion 'I still can't drive past a yellow field without smiling'.

Relaxation

Initially, this is a discussion of what works for individual parents; from loud music in the car to 'retail therapy'; from exercise to watching a sunset. Differing approaches to relaxation suit different individuals. The group also considers, if 'avoidance depletes energy' then is the reverse—focusing, or *wallowing* in grief as it has been disparagingly termed—nurturing and therapeutic? I suspect it is. Deliberate trawls through the photo albums with emotive music on in the background may well feel like wallowing, but it is possible to weave such moments into the fabric of living and welcome the restorative quality of them.

Finally, the session concludes with a guided visualisation or simply a time of reflection during a piece of music. The atmosphere of this session is generally peaceful and calm, so it is not unexpected that the gentle moments of quiet thought at the conclusion should allow some tears to fall, but it is an advantage of the maturing group consensus that these are likely to be far less self-conscious expressions than might have been experienced six months previously.

Session seven

In addition to the familiar tree-blobs, parents are asked whether any of them actually *did* watch a pot boil—and, indeed some will have done, and recount their experiences and where their thoughts wandered to.

The session continues with the solemn reminder that there are only two more sessions to follow, and a rationalisation of why the final three sessions are linked. Endings are particularly difficult for bereaved people, carrying the resonance of loss and actualising yet another loss—the loss of a group and its companionship. So, the group are forewarned that the last session will endeavour to look beyond the ending of the group, the penultimate session is one where they will be asked to take their courage in both hands and take a long, hard look back—and in this, the seventh session, the intention is to look both backwards and forwards. To examine some of the contrasts, and conflicts, of grief. The losses and discoveries; the hopes and fears; the regrets and wishes.

The flip-chart reappears as parents catalogue some of their losses, in addition to the primary and most significant loss. Thinking particularly of the session on dimensions of loss, parents record that they have lost existential qualities, such as confidence, identity and purpose, as well as more substantial losses like friendship or career. The flip-chart fills with a variety of examples, such as: loss of routine; appointments; contact with hospital and professional staff through the child who died; an heir; pram-pushing and clutter; unconditional love—the list becomes a disturbing testament to the all-consuming impact of grief and child loss. It is acknowledged that the ending of the Stepping Stones group will be another loss.

Conversely, the group then examines discoveries made along the way, often unexpected and surprising discoveries. These often reflected the pragmatic approach taken to life in the wake of child loss where priorities and perceptions had been radically unsettled. Parents offered examples like: new outlook; changed perspective; real friends; compassion; strength; new priorities; new friendships; expertise in their child's condition.

Following the refreshment break, parents were guided to work with a partner—not their own—in completing an evaluation of their contrasting feelings in the areas of fears and hopes, regrets and wishes, and losses and discoveries. This is the first occasion that parents have been directed to work in pairs, and the discussion of such intense and stirring thoughts is a challenge generally well met. A plenary session encourages the pairs to share, without compulsion, some of their thoughts and discussions. Undoubtedly, the most poignant area is that of regret. It is a word that carries such a finality of choice; something we desperately wish had been different yet is established in the unchangeable course of our history. Parents torture themselves sometimes with many regrets: treatment options, holidays delayed and never taken, pleasurable experiences they wish their child had encountered. The 'if only's' of well-meaning parents who could not, despite all their efforts, alter the course of their child's life. Parents are reminded that decisions and choices they sometimes come to regret were certainly made in the best interest of their child at the time. Hindsight can give cruel clarity to options that had entirely unknown outcomes at the time. Looking back will always carry some poignant regrets, but wistful is preferable to bitter.

The group are asked in this session if they would like a compilation of their contact details to be distributed the following month. The option of being excluded from the list was also offered, but rarely chosen.

The metaphor of a broken bone is shared with the group. It seems a bone, once broken and healed is stronger at the point of the break due to over-calcification of the tissue, and unlikely to break in the same place again. This message is affirmed with an Ernest Hemingway quotation from *A Farewell to Arms*:

> '*The world breaks everyone, and afterwards some are strong at the broken places.*'
>
> (Hemingway, 1929)

In the light of this, parents are given their most difficult 'homework' to date. They are requested to bring to the next meeting a significant item that provokes a particular memory of their child that they can share with the rest of the group. This is, indeed, the task from which they would have shied away eight months previously, but the nature of the group integrity has changed, and now they are, with some trepidation, prepared to broadcast their memories. Ideas for 'significant items' are proffered—ideally, not a photograph, rather something special, or silly, that has a story attached. Parents are given the option of writing something if they prefer, and, of course, the choice of declining to participate will always be available to them.

Session eight

After the penultimate perusal of the blobs on the tree, a group photograph is taken. Much has been made of remembrance, souvenirs and symbols during the programme, so the photograph will serve to symbolise group members' participation and completion of a programme that was not without its challenges. Evaluation forms are also distributed for return the following month or by post, if preferred.

The main business of the evening is, of course, giving each participant the opportunity to talk about the item they have brought and its connotations to their memory of their child.

Unquestionably, this is the most emotional and poignant session of Stepping Stones and the facilitators acknowledge the achievement parents have made to reach this point. It is probably the most tearful session, but also the most uplifting and affirming, and I fully endorse, without apology, the overt sentimentality of it. We live in a cynical age where tears and displays of emotion are often seen as weakness, and yet those who are able to address and reveal their most painful of feelings must surely be the 'strong' ones.

In the time that I was facilitating the programmes, no parent who had stayed the course ever forgot to bring an item or declined to participate. One bereaved father who was determined his wife would speak for both of them could not resist interjecting and eventually contributed more than she did.

In order to deal impartially with the understandable apprehension parents experienced, names were drawn in random sequence and members told their stories—often struggling to keep within the allotted time scale that ensured every member had their opportunity.

The memories shared were often funny, always moving, and received with great respect by the rest of the group. Even after several years, if I come across the name of a former client who participated in Stepping Stones, I can often recall the item they brought and the story they told. I recall a father who brought a rubber glove and explained how his four-year-old daughter would wear it on her head and perform a chicken dance. A mother who brought building bricks and described how her son loved to build a tower taller than himself, then knock it down. A father who brought a light sabre and recalled how he and his son would dance around the kitchen in the darkness, sabres glowing. And I recall the shy and reticent father whose wife had brought an assortment of memories, assuming she would speak on behalf of both of them, but as she finished, the father produced a large bunch of keys, which, unbeknownst to his wife, he kept with him because their young son had loved to collect keys. Many more reminiscences were revealed over the series of groups and on each occasion it was clear that parents, despite their initial trepidation, felt immense satisfaction at having been able to describe their child so uniquely, either without or despite tears.

At the conclusion of the session, the group address lists would be distributed, the date of the next meeting confirmed, with a reminder that it would be the final session.

Session nine

The final session contains difficult tasks. Many of those attending feel they have only just reached a point of more stability and confidence and now the scaffolding is to be taken away. Others are relieved that they survived the course, but are reluctant to abandon new, but intimate, friendships that have evolved. The session rests within the positive doctrine that 'endings are beginnings' and that principle is affirmed throughout the meeting.

Tree blobs are visited, mercifully, for the last time—with one bereaved father once asserting 'I've cut the damn tree down'. The group photographs from the previous month are distributed. The quality of the photograph is immaterial; it is simply a reminder that they participated in a challenging programme, made some friends, and stayed the course.

The group then revisit their fears and expectations of the very first session, nine months previously (carefully preserved by the facilitators). There are rueful smiles as group members recollect their concerns about 'having to talk' or 'feeling silly if upset'. Expectations may not have been met in the format anticipated—'finding people who understand' might well have occurred, but 'feeling better' has been discovered to be an uncertainty that may vary from day to day; but perhaps, eventually, the good days will outnumber the bad.

To highlight the 'endings are beginnings' theme the group are introduced to the Lifecircle model that I based on observations and information from the experience of bereaved parents.

All change incorporates elements of loss. Observing the expedition that bereaved parents were undertaking, I realised that the continuing attachment to their deceased child would indubitably impact on the rest of their life. Parents often said 'you never get over it, you just get used to it', implicitly expressing the entwining of their deceased child's life—and death—with the rest of their family story. The following representation evolved then out of the understanding that change is an inevitable part of life; all living things change, it is a definition of life. Most changes, however, carry elements of loss—some barely significant and some bringing devastating anguish. The tragic losses will result in grief, but those who grieve will also discover new things, as evidenced in

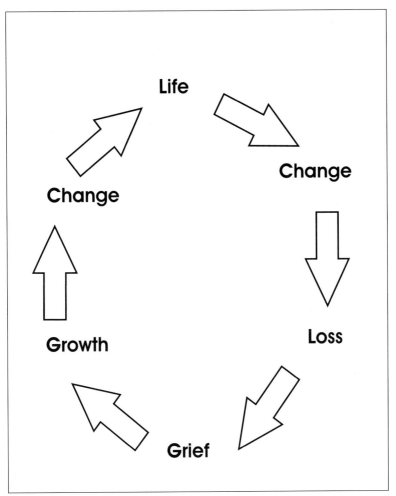

Lifecircle

the previous month's discussion on losses and discoveries, even if it is only the hitherto unimagined depths of the pain of loss. With new discoveries there are elements of growth, and when an organism grows, it changes. Thus the cycle is complete, only to be repeated again and again throughout life; for we cannot experience changes without some losses, and as long as we live, we are compelled to change. For bereaved parents the diagram itself is probably inconsequential. What they instinctively appreciate is that their child has impacted, and will continue to impact on the rest of the parents' lives. This does not have to be seen in the negative sense of unremitting grief, but is an acknowledgement of that child's existence; their place in the world. It can never be as if that child had never been.

So the life and death of their child will be inextricably interwoven into each parent's life. It is impossible not to be changed by such a traumatic event and the changes in these parents, and other family members, will be a permanent testament and legacy from their child who died. No life, however short, is insignificant, and the ripple effect of each child's life will continue on into eternity. As Stepping Stones concludes, so life after 'the bereaved parents' group' begins and having endured the hardest loss of all, these parents will hopefully be equipped to survive some of life's more minor losses—like the ending of a support group.

After the much needed refreshments, group members take time to participate in an activity whereby, after passing around sheets of paper and concealing each additional message, each member of the group eventually receives a collection of, hopefully encouraging, statements or wishes from the rest of the group—to be read later, when alone. Group members insisted on including the facilitators in this activity and I treasure the resulting lists of messages. Some are extremely insulting jibes in revenge for what some perceived as nine months of torture, but often even the insults concealed thanks or fond farewells. One bereaved father insisted on calling me 'the chief onion-peeler' because of the constant stripping of protective emotional layers he felt he'd had to endure. His message therefore read, 'To the chief onion-peeler. As much as I take the piss sometimes, you've no idea how much help you've been to me.'

The group concludes with a reminder that they are at liberty to continue meeting informally, as friends, but the organisation of that is entirely in the hands of group members. It is a challenging and difficult time for facilitators who are likely to experience something akin to urging baby birds out of the nest. For the counsellor/facilitator it is a moment of serious contemplation about thinly disguised inclinations to rescue, and an issue that is likely to be explored in subsequent supervision sessions.

Finally, as group members leave their closing session they are given a stone—yet another symbol—to remember the time spent, and discoveries made, at Stepping Stones.

Evaluations

After each session the facilitators will have met to discuss and dissect the programme and group responses. Sometimes elements of the course would be readjusted in response to participator feedback or issues that had spontaneously arisen in the course of a session. The basic framework of the programme has remained the same for some years, but flexibility to accommodate participants' needs or suggestions is a feature of the series.

After the final session there are the more formal evaluations of group members to examine. In these, parents were asked to comment on:

- the venue
- the timing
- the room
- childcare, if applicable
- the facilitators
- the usefulness of each session (sessions were listed as a reminder)
- any other comments or suggestions.

There is often a positive bias within evaluations from bereaved families, as they can feel a debt of gratitude to those who remained alongside and supported them when, perhaps, other support structures were crumbling or not materialising. It is predictable, therefore, that criticism—even constructive criticism— did not form a large part of the evaluations.

Three evaluations received commented that they would have preferred the group to run for longer. One respondent felt the 'tree-blob' checking-in mechanism had been too personal at times. Two respondents (whose groups had been reduced in numbers of participants) felt that a larger group would have offered more variety and opportunity for friendships. All other comments were disconcertingly positive, but must be interpreted in the light of the comments above. Some extracts included:

'Thank you for all the love, support and fun we have shared over the last few months.'

'Thank you for your kindness, empathy and imagination. I was afraid it would be like Alcoholics Anonymous, but it never was. You struck a good balance between levity and seriousness. I'll never forget this time. I always felt at home, it's a very peaceful place.'

'I didn't really want to come—but I'm glad I did! I think it made me feel I'm not on my own and all the emotions I feel are quite normal. Thanks.'

'The meetings have been really useful. It's comforting to be able to say "yes I can feel this way!"'

Behind the appreciative gratitude of their comments, many of the parents clearly repeat some principles of bereavement support that are being clarified by current theorists and will, hopefully, permeate the rest of society in the coming years. The recurring themes appear to be;

- *Permission*: allow grievers their feelings without dictating to them how a theorist or counsellor suggests they should be

- *Listen*: allow those who grieve to share their stories. The potency of narrative opportunities has come to the fore in many fields and it is certainly vital to healthy grieving

- *Honesty*: do not offer a facade, or expect to be greeted by one. All feelings, expressions and thoughts can have their validity

- *Continuing bonds*: perhaps more relevant to the loss of a child than the loss an older relative (Parkes *et al*, 2000), but bereaved parents often seem determined to maintain their connection to their deceased child through narrative, remembrance, memorialisation and celebration.

On a wider scale, the programme also proffers several unanswered questions to add to the many debates within the field of bereavement support:

- What about the 50 per cent of parents who choose not to join a group initiative? What are their reasons and what is their comparative grief process?

- Is the programme transferable or does it sit uniquely within the situation of a children's hospice with the advantage of prior encounters with families?

- Is the length of the programme appropriate to organisations that may not be in a position to offer pre- and post-group support?

- Would further research identify the ingredient that enabled an unusually high uptake by bereaved fathers?

References

Bowlby J (1969) *Attachment and Loss*. Basic Books, New York

Clare A (2000) *Masculinity in Crisis*. Chatto and Windus, London.

Davies AM (2001) Death of adolescents: parental grief and coping strategies. *Br J Nurs* **10**: 13–24

Doka KJe (1995) *Children Mourning, Mourning Children*. Hospice Foundation of America, Washington

Field D, Hockey J, Small N (1997) *Death, Gender and Ethnicity*. Routledge, London

Gibran K (1991) *The Prophet*. Macmillan, London

Hemingway E (1929) *A Farewell to Arms*. Jonathan Cape, London

Humphrey GM, Zimpfer D (1996) *Counselling for Grief and Bereavement*. Sage, London

Irwin M, Pike J (1993) Bereavement, depressive symptoms and immune function. In: Stroebe M, Stroebe W, Hansson RO, eds. *Handbook of Bereavement Theory, Research and Intervention*. University of Cambridge Press, Cambridge

Jacobs M (2002) *Psychodynamic Counselling in Action*. Sage, London

Klass D (1999) *The Spiritual Lives of Bereaved Parents*. Taylor Francis, Philadelphia

Kubler-Ross E (1970) *On Death and Dying*. Routledge, London

Kuykendall J (1998) (Ed, Potts, S.) London, pp. Masterclass.

Lendrum S, Syme G (1992) *The Gift of Tears*. Routledge, London

Parkes CM, Relf M, Couldrick A (1996) *Counselling in Terminal Care and Bereavement*. BPS Books, Leicester

Parkes CM, Shannon P, Edgeworth S (2000) Sixth International Conference on grief and bereavement in contemporary society. *Bereavement Care* **19**: 45–46

Rochford G (1991) Theory, concepts, feelings and practice: The contemplation of bereavement within a social work course. In: Lishman J, ed. *Handbook of Theory for Practice Teachers in Social Work*. Jessica Kingsley, London

Rosenblatt PC (2000) Parents talking in the present tense about their dead child. *Bereavement Care* **19**: 35–38

Rowa-Dewar N (2002) Do interventions make a difference to bereaved parents: a systematic review of controlled studies. *Int J Pall Nurs* **8**: 452–57

Stroebe M, Schut H (1995) The Dual Process mo9del of coping with loss. In: *International Workgroup on Death, Dying and Bereavement*, Oxford, UK

7

The Treasure Weekend: supporting bereaved siblings

Society has remained largely unconvinced or unable to realise the benefits of allowing bereaved children to focus on grief and loss, believing or fearing that the child's grief might be exacerbated. Historically, children were often assumed to be relatively unaffected by a death in their family, or were presumed to have innate capabilities for regeneration that ensured their lives continued unhampered by grief. These assumptions often led to children's grief being overlooked and discounted, as the title of Pennels and Smith book, *The Forgotten Mourners*, (1995), suggested. Society, and consequently bereaved parents, could assure themselves that they were appropriately shielding their surviving children from 'adult' traumas by concealing the worst of their own grief, thus tentatively and hopefully professing that the children had none. Parkes *et al* noted that bereaved children are more supported through involvement and open discussion than through exclusion and denial (Parkes *et al*, 1996). Knowledge and understanding of children's grief have developed substantially in recent years and it is now established that some children who are denied the right to mourn may suffer debilitating consequences of unresolved grief (Black, 1996; Worden, 1996). The loss of a sibling is a particularly isolating experience for children, as most bereaved young people's first experience of the loss of a close relative is the death of a grandparent or parent. Sibling death holds unique challenges as it impacts upon the emotional and psychological developmental future of the surviving siblings. There may be many ramifications for the bereaved child; their position in the family will have changed—perhaps their older sibling died and they find themselves now the eldest living child, a position they neither anticipated nor desired. Perhaps the youngest member of a family died, leaving surviving siblings with a premature awareness of the fragility of life at a time when most children do not have to encounter such harsh realities. For the parents of these children, grieving will inevitably undermine their parenting skills and family security will be to some extent, at least temporarily, destabilised. Children's reactions to death and loss are described in more detail in the chapter on bereaved children, but hospice professionals' awareness of the difficulties bereaved siblings face resulted in a determination to offer, within our programmes of support interventions, some contributions that were specifically designed for bereaved siblings.

Each year at Derian House, a residential weekend is offered as part of the menu of support interventions for bereaved siblings. This venture, the Treasure Weekend, was planned and initiated by the hospice staff and is very much a team effort where nursing and care staff, as well as bereavement support staff, participate enthusiastically in a weekend that sensitively combines memorialisation of children who died with the affirmation of a surviving sibling's evolving journey of life. The Treasure Weekend derives its name from the intention to supply each child with a 'Treasure Box'—a designated container in which to collect and keep items of particular significance associated with their deceased sibling.

The venue would be Derian House itself, as this environment not only offered a breadth of facilities for well siblings to avail themselves of, but also afforded opportunity for reminiscence of earlier visits with a sick sibling. The scheduled weekend would remain as free as possible from respite bookings, although emergency respite or terminal care was necessarily available if required. As the hospice incorporates nine large bedrooms and four self-contained flats, we were able to utilise the entire hospice for the residential requirements of the Treasure Weekends, which have never exceeded twenty-four children in attendance. Some staff, with a view to maintaining continuity of care, chose to be resident throughout the weekend and many staff who lived locally participated in the full programme also. A rota of waking night staff was continued, as usual, throughout the weekend, although duties differed significantly from the customary nursing care of sick children. There is a substantial variation between nine sick children who are inclined to be fairly passive during late evening and overnight, and twenty or more active, excited siblings who—as well as their moments of quiet reflection—have a lot of boisterous energy to expend.

Prior to the weekend, parents and children were contacted by a letter explaining the purpose of the weekend and inviting parental permission for those children who agreed to attend. Each year the siblings who had been bereaved in the previous fifteen months (but not the three months immediately prior to the weekend) would be invited. The response to the initial weekend was remarkable in that all siblings contacted chose to attend. Subsequent years drew similar responses, with children only missing the weekend if they had prior, unavoidable commitments. This alone reflects the requirement of young people to be validated as grievers. It also indicates an immense gesture of trust from parents who were willing to allow their very precious surviving children to spend a weekend away from parental oversight and return to a place that perhaps held sad, as well as happy, memories. Parents, understandably, have an inclination to overprotect their surviving children (Worden, 1991) and would probably prefer to avoid the pain of believing that children can and do suffer emotional distress. Once this reality was acknowledged, however, families could find strength in the honesty of their relationships and a unity within their family dynamic as they faced the future together.

Before the Treasure Weekend, all prospective attendees would be visited by the Family Support Co-ordinator in order to establish each child's understanding of their loss and to discuss any reservations or anxieties the children may have had. It also gave children themselves opportunity to impact on the programme as they shared their own thoughts of how they would like to remember their sibling. As the event was to be held at Derian House, there was noted enthusiasm expressed by the Treasure Weekenders who, generally, had very positive recollections of the hospice and appreciated the facilities they had been able to utilise during the course of their brother or sister's illness. A frequently asked question on the preparatory visits was 'Will we be able to swim in the pool?'—evidence that recollections of the hospice were not entirely occupied with terminal illness.

Nearer the time for the Treasure Weekend, children were given an outline programme for the weekend and advised to bring casual clothing, suited to the varied activities to be undertaken. There is no cost to families for the weekend. Staff consolidated the aims of the Treasure Weekend into:

- Remembering the 'forgotten mourners' and acknowledging them as grievers
- Providing a safe, comfortable and supportive environment for expression of all feelings connected with the loss of a sibling
- Giving permission for both looking back and looking forward
- Creating and collating items of remembrance (Treasures)
- Meeting with other bereaved siblings
- Maintaining links with the hospice as a source of support.

Children and young people attending the Treasure Weekend have been between the ages of five and eighteen years. Much consideration was given to the formation of age-related groups within the attendees. The ultimate decision, endorsed by subsequent evaluation and experience, was to divide youngsters into mixed age groups for workshops. We were well aware of the wide age range and consequent variations in understanding and expression that we might encounter, but were confident that the presence of older children offers young children some security, confidence and assistance in activities, while the presence of younger children offers older ones the opportunity to simplify their thinking, participate in activities they may have eschewed if alone with their peers, and extend their cognisance of the implications of bereavement. Our confidence proved to be well founded.

The second Treasure Weekend introduced a dilemma we had not previously considered. Among that year's cluster of bereaved siblings was John, a young man who himself suffered from the same life-limiting condition from which his brother had died. Was there a rationale for allowing a 'patient', a recurring hospice user, to attend the Treasure Weekend? The rationale, of course, was that we could not overlook his status as a bereaved brother and he was duly invited. He readily accepted and the weekend proved something of a watershed for him. From being relatively withdrawn, with a latent depression that was cleverly disguised as adolescent hostility, John discovered a wicked sense of humour and the ability to converse. Our concerns for him reduced as the weekend progressed and he clearly indicated that he had another 'special need'—to be acknowledged and validated as a bereaved brother.

The Treasure Weekend Programme

The weekend runs from late Friday afternoon to Sunday afternoon. The programme is carefully and deliberately intended to incorporate both memory work and pure leisure pursuits. Implicit in every aspect of the programme are permission and honesty—permission to remember, to grieve, or to walk away. Children are aware before they arrive that death and bereavement are on the agenda, and because these 'taboo' issues are acknowledged with a candour that is generally avoided in society, they are reduced to a manageable size.

The children's first activity on arrival is to make a name-badge for themselves, learning each other's names being an inherent part of building up trust and confidence in a newly formed group. Then, each arriving child is given a sock, with the instruction to locate the child carrying the matching partner to the pair. It must be confessed that these socks have usually been cunningly manipulated to ensure that children meet a child they may be sharing a room with. They are required to ask their newly discovered partner some inane questions such as their most despised vegetable. However, the *raison d'etre* of the weekend was not lost on even our youngest participants. One six-year-old was overheard asking her fellow sock-holder, 'So who died in your family?'

When all the youngsters have arrived the first group meeting is held, commencing with games establishing what children have in common. This leads inexorably to the conclusion that, sadly, the commonality that constitutes the focus of the weekend is having a brother or sister who died. Evaluations have revealed that one of the overwhelming benefits of the weekend is for children to encounter other youngsters who have lost a sibling. It is satisfying that child death figures have reduced considerably over the last century, but the consequence for a surviving sibling in the twenty-first century can be that they might be the only child in an entire school who has lost a *young* member of their family, and this can be a very isolating experience. The relief at encountering an entire group of other bereaved siblings is almost palpable, even in the initial hours of the Treasure Weekend. Further trust games enhance the group cohesiveness and any remaining reservations are usually beginning to dissipate.

Having established a few house rules for the weekend (largely health and safety measures), the first evening concludes with a programme of games and activities—including swimming for those who choose—to release some of the nervous tension and simmering energy that may have accrued during preparation and arrival. By suppertime and bedtime, it seems these youngsters have known each other for days rather than a few hours. Naturally, some of the children may well have encountered other families on previous visits to the hospice, but it is more often the case that children were not acquainted with one another prior to the weekend.

The following morning effervescent children and bleary-eyed teenagers (reluctantly foregoing their customary Saturday morning lie-in) connect over breakfast and gather their energies for the day ahead. The programme continues with a series of three workshops through which the children rotate: art, music, and words (once called 'drama' but language became the focal point).

Art

Probably the busiest, most varied and most popular workshop, the Art room becomes a hive of activity as children encounter the range of choices available to them. A consistent feature is the sunflower collage, whereby children design and make their own sunflower to add to the prepared backdrop. Some highly imaginative creations have been known to appear and the finished collage adorns the dining room wall of the hospice until it is replaced by the artistic endeavours of the next year's collection. Most of the activities carry elements of remembrance—either of a brother or sister who died, or of friendships made during the Treasure Weekend. Children may choose from a selection of activities including:

- *Salt sculptures*: in small glass jars, layering up coloured portions of salt (coloured by grinding chalks into the salt) with perhaps a sibling's favourite colours, school uniform colours, or the colours of a football team

- *Memory mobiles*: hanging mobiles decorated with symbolic drawings or messages, coloured ribbons, reminders of a deceased sibling's favourite band or sport or TV programme

- *Friendship bracelets*: the weaving of coloured threads that have proven so popular with youngsters as a gesture of alliance or remembrance

- *Pottery*: an opportunity to experiment on the potter's wheel and make some impressive creations that are later fired and glazed and returned to the youngsters. A wonderful, encouraging and patient potter comes in to guide and assist the children—I recall hearing him once tell a child who felt their feeble attempts at pottery had gone disastrously wrong, 'There's no such thing as wrong in art. It's just gone another way'

- *Handprint pictures or collages*: the personal satisfaction that is derived from seeing one's handprint become a colourful work of art

- *Glass painting*: each youngster decorates their own candleholder that will be used later in the weekend

- *Painting*: simply free creativity for those who want to express themselves in that way

- *Face-painting, hair-braiding, transfers*, stickers and an endless flow of glue, glitter, paper and threads all combine to offer a veritable cornucopia of choices for the youngsters.

And all the time, they chatter. They talk with their peers, they talk with staff, they talk to themselves... and conversations about death, loss, and grief interweave among the moments of hilarity and excited squeals of achievement.

The Play Specialist at the hospice also designed a booklet, entitled 'My Special Book', which younger children particularly enjoy completing. It affirms the reality of their personhood—not only as a 'bereaved' or 'surviving' sibling, but also as a unique personality in their own right.

It is remarkable how loquacious children can be when embroiled in a creative activity, a point that should not be lost on those who embark on counselling with children. The discomfort of a one-to-one encounter is much relieved for a child when they can be concurrently occupied with some activity that permits them to avert their gaze and feel less conspicuous.

Some of the activities were suggested through the work of the 'Winston's Wish' organisation who offer support to children bereaved of an immediate family member (Stokes and Crossley, 1995). Additional activities reflect the gifts and talents of a diverse hospice team who relish the opportunity to extend their holistic principles of care into the realm of bereavement support. There is an abundance of artwork of various shapes and sizes as a result of this workshop and items are left safely to dry or set as the children move on to their next workshop.

Music

The hospice was fortunate in procuring the services of a music therapist and this session is their territory. The children have a selection of instruments to choose from, mostly percussion, requiring little or no musical skill and these are utilised to the full in this workshop. It includes considering communication without words—what suggests a particular piece of music is dreamy, sad, energetic, happy? Children are encouraged to reflect on how they use music as an *aide memoire* or a mood enhancer. Frivolous games are included, like passing a musical message around the circle of participants, not unlike Chinese whispers. A series of feelings, compiled by the youngsters, are listed on a flip-chart and then the group attempts to portray each feeling using music, with whatever instruments they have to hand.

A game of hunt-the-sweetie adds some levity as children play their instruments loudly or quietly depending on whether the 'hunter' is nearer or further from the hidden treasure. The workshop epitomises the ethos of the weekend in that the dual motifs of remembrance and recreation are offered equal prominence. Conversations may evolve about music remembered from funerals, or the favourite bands of a deceased sibling. Music is a powerful, emotive trigger to memories and recollections of both sad times and happy times, so the session is well located within the weekend's programme.

Words

The final workshop examines vocabularies and literature. Narrative processes are to the fore and youngsters are encouraged to consider the words and language utilised to discuss death and grief. A somewhat flippant examination of various death-related euphemisms ensues, with youngsters gleefully making diverse weird and wonderful additions to the terminology. Phrases like 'kick the bucket', 'passed over', 'gone to sleep', 'no longer with us', 'safe in the arms of Jesus', 'gone away', and many others are dissected and interpreted—with the intriguing conclusion that the word least used yet most understood by children is 'dead'. This may seem a somewhat morbid and tasteless discussion, but the reality is that young people are both fascinated and confused by society's efforts to cloak reality with obscure gobbledygook, and they appreciate honest and uncomplicated explanations. Language can be either a deliberate or an inadvertent means of excluding children, but a process of inclusion is far more therapeutic.

The workshop also unfolds Doris Stickney's classic story about death, *Waterbugs and Dragonflies* (Stickney, 1982). This, too, is a euphemism, consisting as it does of the analogous tale of waterbugs who are not able to return below water once they evolve into dragonflies—and thus cannot tell their former friends what has happened to them. However, it recounts gracefully the unknowingness of death and whatever lies beyond and although written within a Christian context, the story itself can relate powerfully across cultures and age ranges. The imagery is not lost on the young people and they enact their own version of the tale using model bugs and dragonflies in their narration. The session concludes with an activity about epitaphs. Children are not usually included in such decisions, so the youngsters are offered the opportunity to write what they would have chosen, had the choice been theirs, for their brother or sister's headstone. Some touching and thoughtful prose appears; examples below with their original spelling:

> *I really, really miss you. I hope you have made some new frens in Heaven.*

> *Remembering you is very upsetting but you should remember no matter how upseting it is, I will never forget you, starting from when I was born.*

Throughout all the workshops members of staff are available to support children individually, or allow them to take time apart from the group if they choose.

With its proliferation of activities and some profound messages, Saturday morning is quite intense, both intellectually and emotionally. Therefore, the rest of Saturday is surrendered to pure enjoyment, including a healthy expenditure of physical energy. Weather permitting, various outdoor games feature, including a bouncy castle, team games, parachute games, ball games, moving on later to a treasure hunt, a barbecue, Karaoke sessions, and finally viewing a film together. Younger members of the group have been known to fall asleep at this point, and it is noted with some relief that *all* of the group seem to settle very gratefully and speedily into their bedrooms on the second night.

Sunday morning commences with a rather more leisurely breakfast reflecting both the efforts of the previous day and the comfortable atmosphere that has developed over the weekend.

Following breakfast, children are given time to complete any creative ventures of the previous morning, and to prepare for the 'improvised' memorial service that will include both visual and verbal contributions, if they so choose.

The culmination of the weekend is the memorial and celebration service. Children and young people are invited to display their artwork, read their poems, choose some music and devise a unique celebration of their weekend's endeavours. Treasure boxes are chosen and distributed and youngsters begin to gather items they may have created for inclusion in the box. The Treasure Weekend participants are also presented with a memorial book, with a page assigned to each represented child who has died. Youngsters can add their own message to their page, be it either literal or pictorial. The hospice maintains an 'adult' version of these books with calligraphed names and family contributions. There is no disputing the delight when even the very youngest children are told they may add something to the Treasure Weekend book and their spelling or writing ability is not a consideration. The entries reflect the range of age groups in attendance, with some of the youngest contributors offering perhaps the most poignant messages, often illustrated with rainbows, angels or flowers. Older participants will pen considered and profound thoughts, but the predominant message that permeates the pages seems to be 'I will always miss you'. The simple truth that a brother or sister who once took their place within a family composition may not feature in future family portraits, but whose absence will never go unnoticed.

The more structured portion of the service is unfurled with all participants seated in a circle and given their candle to light. The candles are lit, one from another, around the circle with most youngsters remembering aloud the name of their brother or sister as they light the flame. These are undoubtedly the most poignant moments of the weekend, and not without tears—but there is a rewarding impression of unity and acceptance ensuring that tears are never greeted with surprise or derision. Some time is spent contemplating the flickering flames, with the comparison that, just as it is impossible to really see the edge of a constantly flickering flame, so it is impossible to see the 'edge' of love—and when someone we love dies, that does not necessarily mark the end of our love for them.

After extinguishing the candles, children are given helium filled balloons with a ribbon and card attached. They may write a message on the card, thoughts that they may want to share purely between themselves and their brother or sister who died, for these messages will be read by no one and are to be simply released.

Indeed, the messages never have been read by any of the adult helpers, so cannot and would not be recounted here.

The group, clutching balloons, then move to the gardens and the balloons are released. It is a symbolic gesture that is by no means unique to children's hospice work, but it also resonates once again with the relief youngsters have experienced in the realisation that they are not alone in sibling loss. A cluster of balloons float upwards, just as a cluster of young people gaze after them and, for a time at least, the isolation of their unusual bereaved status is appeased by the solidarity of a group.

The memorial service is followed immediately by a picnic lunch, giving opportunity to restore some equilibrium and enabling staff to mingle with the children and ensure that emotions remain intact. With the glorious facility that youngsters have to swiftly acclimatise to fluctuating moods, the atmosphere soon reverts to levity and smiles. This is not to trivialise the solemnity of what has gone before, but simply reflects and endorses the natural capacity children have to cope with the many and varied emotional facets a day can bring. It also reiterates the ethos of the weekend. The intention is for children to receive permission to be sad, and permission to be happy. Permission to look back, and permission to look forward.

After lunch the children reassemble for some esteem-building activities, closure work, and the ubiquitous evaluation forms. The final session also includes the distribution of 'goody-bags' with some explanation regarding the contents. Some of the items within the bag are simply gifts, small mementoes of a weekend spent together, but a couple of items have particular significance. Each child receives a potted sunflower to take home and plant. The sunflower testifies to the cycle of nature—it will, hopefully, grow and blossom through the summer, but when it fades in autumn and darkens, becoming a mere shadow of its former glory, it will yet contain many seeds that can be kept for growing the following year.

Each bag also contains a mirror. This is to remind our young participants that a mirror can be used, as in a car, to look back in order to travel safely forwards. This is the message of the Treasure Weekend that we hope children will retain. Permission to look back, but also permission to travel safely onwards.

Soon afterwards parents return to collect their children. The anxiety and curiosity of parents who surrendered their children to a weekend focused upon bereavement are to be anticipated, and a letter is distributed advising parents to allow their fairly weary progeny to tell them as much or as little of the weekend as they choose. A tall order for parents who must surely be impatient to interrogate their youngsters and ensure they were not overly distressed by the weekend. Yet subsequent feedback from both children and parents suggests that the advice is largely adhered to. A mother informed me shortly after a Treasure Weekend that her daughter had spent her first night home tearfully talking about her sadness over her sister's death, leaving the mother highly ambivalent about allowing her daughter's attendance at the weekend. I awaited the inevitable criticism and castigation for having reopened old wounds, but it transpired that the following morning this mother found her daughter to be brighter and more amenable than she had been for some time, causing the mother to conclude that if the Treasure Weekend had given the child permission to ventilate feelings and thoughts that she had hitherto concealed, it had served a useful and therapeutic purpose.

The Treasure Weekend undergoes a three-fold evaluation process with contributions from the children, the staff and parents. The children's evaluation forms are very basic, consisting of some simple statements including:

1. The best thing about the weekend was   …………………………..............

2. The worst thing about the weekend was   …………………………..............

3. I'd just like to say   …………………………..............

I was particularly fond of an evaluation that read:

The best thing about the weekend was making friends and swimming.
The worst thing about the weekend was the candles and balloons
I'd just like to say I had a great time

This, and similar responses, encapsulated the view that children could acknowledge that sadness is difficult and yet it did not detract from their overall enjoyment of the weekend. Permission to be sad and permission to be happy, the simplest suggestion I can offer to those who wish to support bereaved children.

For subsequent Treasure Weekend evaluation forms, the third statement was amended to 'Any other thoughts…..', as it was noted that an inordinate amount of youngsters had responded to the original phrasing with 'thank you' and staff feared politeness was obscuring the participants' opportunity to make a more personal statement. Generally though, children's evaluations tend to be disarmingly honest. None expressed regret over joining the weekend, and all requested a reunion. A 'Treasureday Reunion' is indeed held approximately eight months later where the focus is less upon bereavement and more upon rekindling friendships made at the Treasure Weekend.

Staff evaluations combine with a de-brief immediately following the departure of the children. It is unquestionably an emotionally draining experience for practitioners, despite the associated satisfaction and fulfilment. There is a need to ventilate feelings as well as examining responses to the programme in more detail. A subsequent reflective meeting some days later offers an arena for clarifying thoughts and suggesting possible amendments to the programme or the preparations for the next year.

Home visits are made in the ensuing weeks both to discover parents' thoughts, responses, suggestions or concerns, and also to meet once more with the children who attended. Families generally conceded a greater openness in their conversations and attitudes around death, loss and bereavement. They shared, with their children, the belief that encountering other bereaved siblings had been an enlightening and reassuring experience for the children. It is impossible to draw resolute conclusions from relatively anecdotal feedback, and this area evidently suggests itself for further practitioner research. However, the prevailing impression gained from all three evaluations is that the intervention is worthwhile and children and their families are appreciative of the support offered.

During one post-Treasure Weekend home visit, I encountered a young boy who proudly fetched his Treasure Box to show me how carefully he was safeguarding its contents. He meticulously explained the significance of each item in the box and with a final flourish pronounced, 'And I've still got my mirror safe!' 'Wonderful,' I responded, 'can you remember what the mirror was about?' 'Oh yes,' he replied, 'look back and keep going!'

I was so delighted with his succinct paraphrase of my message that it almost became the title of this book. The ethos of the Treasure Weekend had remained with him—it is acceptable to reflect and be sad sometimes, but it is equally acceptable to look forward with excited anticipation.

References

Black D (1996) Childhood bereavement. *Br Med J* **312**: 1496

Parkes CM, Relf M, Couldrick A (1996) *Counselling in Terminal Care and Bereavement*. BPS books, Leicester

Pennels M, Smith S (1995) *The Forgotten Mourners*. Jessica Kingsley, London

Stickney D (1982) *Waterbugs and Dragonflies*. Cassell, London

Stokes J, Crossley D (1995) Camp Winston: A residential intervention with bereaved children. In: Smith SC, Pennells M, eds. *Interventions with Bereaved Children*. Jessica Kingsley, London

Worden JW (1996) *Children and Grief*. Guildford Press, New York

Worden JW (1991) *Grief Counselling and Grief Therapy*, 2nd edn. Routledge, London

8

Cornerstones: a support group for bereaved grandparents

Having established support programmes for bereaved siblings and parents, the hospice team realised in due course that there was another generation of grievers who were being overlooked. Grandparents hold a unique position within families bereaved of a young child; the pain of losing a grandchild is exacerbated by the achingly incurable frustration of being unable to shield their adult child from the devastating loss. Grandparents, perhaps more so than bereaved siblings, are often the forgotten mourners within the scenario, frequently assumed to be one generation distanced from the grief—or sufficiently mature to be somehow accustomed to death and loss. This is a sad misrepresentation of their position, for the effects of loss are cumulative and maturity does not necessarily herald an emotional resilience; rather, it may increase vulnerability. While empathy and support are directed towards younger generations, bereaved grandparents may find scant opportunity to verbalise or even reveal their grief, thus becoming progressively more inclined towards the depressing consequences of unaddressed grief.

The hospice undertook to offer a programme of support to bereaved grandparents, similar in style to the Stepping Stones programme for parents, but of slightly shorter duration and with a content more appropriate to grandparents. As some grandparents were retired while others were still in employment, the timing of sessions was negotiated carefully to suit each specific group. Most sessions were held in an evening, but certain groups found daytime attendance preferable. To continue the 'stones' theme of Stepping Stones and Pebbles, the group was called Cornerstones. I must confess to an initial suggestion of Cobbles, but that was derisively voted down as somewhat ageist and derogatory—although one bereaved father whose mother was to attend Cornerstones suggested we might like to call the group Loose Slates!

Cornerstones it was—and appropriately so, as the older generation are very often the cornerstone of a family's stability, assisting with child care and other support, particularly where a family is contending with the terminal illness of a child. The first Cornerstones group was something of an experiment as there was no way of predicting the response we would get from this older generation. Although I was aware that bereavement support for grandparents tended to be very limited, I was also concerned that the cultural and attitudinal differences for this generation might preclude their participation in 'talking therapies' or group encounters *per se*. I suspected that many of those over fifty-five might adhere more closely to the 'least said, soonest mended' philosophy of former years and regard communal discussions of feelings and emotions with a modicum of distaste. My suspicions were completely unfounded—alternatively, it can be assumed that those to whom group encounters were anathema did not choose to attend a Cornerstones group. However, these were in the minority. For the first group, seventeen grandparents were invited, and fifteen arrived. Like Stepping Stones, these were to be closed groups, but of shorter duration. The programme extended over five weeks as the more irregular lifestyle—and more frequent holidays—of some grandparents prohibited pro- grammes that spanned several months.

Predictably, the first group of grandparents did indeed arrive with the same sense of trepidation with which their adult children may have attended the first Stepping Stones group. However, within minutes the level of conversation was such that they barely required a facilitator. It was as if the floodgates had been opened and the repressed thoughts, feelings and longings of the previous months were given rein. This generation, more than any other, appeared to identify with one another and many freely shared their concerns and frustrations within the family's grief journey. I was profoundly moved as, in response to a question from one of the grandmothers present, each member of the group conceded their unremitting survivor guilt. They—even more than the parents—expected to predecease the child and most, if not all, grandparents would willingly have exchanged their life for that of a grandchild. It was noticeable that many grandparents appeared to age more rapidly following the death of a grandchild, seeming more frail and vulnerable than just a short time before. In common with societal norms, more grandparents professed a religious faith than members of subsequent generations and, despite the burden of grief they bore, some grandparents felt that any fears for the end of their earthly life would be much alleviated by the thought of reunion with a loved grandchild.

Other relics of generational and cultural difference remained, and the Cornerstone attendees had more difficulty grasping the philosophy of 'avoidance depletes energy' than their adult children may have done. They wanted to protect both their adult children and their surviving grandchildren and were initially unconvinced of any therapeutic value in sharing painful feelings of grief across generations. The expectation and determination to 'be strong' were indelibly printed across their consciences, but some softening occurred as they began to understand the merit of congruence and the debilitating deception of a 'strong' exterior that concealed a crushed and hurting interior. Those who attended Cornerstones were quick to criticise contentious issues, but were also eager to learn and understand more about how they, their children, and their children's children might be responding to bereavement. Discussions were animated and articulate and certainly extended my own understanding of generational differences in grief and loss.

We borrowed and adapted several of the Stepping Stones session formats, including the session on dimensions of loss. This introduced particularly stimulating discussion as the grandparents considered the various dimensions of their life that had been impacted by the death of a grandchild—yet not necessarily in the same way that their adult children were affected:

- *Identity*: The confusing and disturbing position for some, of having been a grandparent, but no longer having a grandchild. This could inflict profound suffering when the grandparents had habitually mixed in a peer group that consisted largely of other grandparents. How does their social group manage the transition? No more photographs and anecdotes to share. It is not surprising that many

]grandparentsgrandparents become relatively reclusive in the initial stages of bereavement. Similarly, grandparents are often utilised as carers, particularly for a sick child, when parents have career commitments or other children to consider. Thus the grandparent's identity is closely embroiled with the life of the child they tend. The identity and self-worth of such a bereaved grandparent have been severely damaged

- *Physical*: Grandparents, even more than parents, often seemed physically diminished by the death of a grandchild. The strain was visible, and reflected in an apparently more rapid ageing process. With some, this was temporary and renewed vigour could be witnessed eventually as months and years passed. I suspect, however, that some of the physical vulnerability is closely allied to the 'survivor guilt' that grandparents acknowledged. It is as if the euphemistic 'feeling one's age' becomes more tangible in the aftermath of child death amid the fervent yet hopeless regret that wanted the family deaths to follow the 'correct' generational sequence

- *Emotional*: Changes may well have been wrought in this generation that survived the 'stiff upper lip' years of British history. Adherence to their former belief systems and values may still be possible, but infinitely more costly. For others, they may barely recognise their former self who has been replaced by a far more expressive and effusive grandparent

- *Family/community*: As mentioned above, the bereaved grandparent's place in the community may be largely dependent on whether or not there are any further surviving grandchildren. Without the accoutrements of grandparent-hood, it is difficult to discern the bereaved grandparent's place in the community. Within the family, relationships, even if they were formerly excellent, may well be strained. Those family members who love each other the most will want to make things better for each other—and the frustration of not being able to 'fix' this can lead to irritability and sometimes anger. Paradoxically, they may reject, or be rejected by, those with whom they really want to be close

- *Lifestyle*: This may have changed in respect of their involvement in the care of a sick child. Even if not, the most enviable and luxurious lifestyle of the affluent retired couple who spend months of the year in sunnier climes loses its delight when the shadow of child death appears

- *Spiritual*: As previously noted, adherence to a traditional religious faith is more common within this older generation, although there are still plenty who would denounce any semblance of a deity that allows such untimely deaths. As the generation who still sang hymns and knew Bible stories in their growing years, grandparents are more likely to think of their deceased grandchild in terms of 'angels' and 'Heaven'.

This generation of grievers perhaps drew the most admiration from me. For some of them, the cultural values of their youth had been slowly obliterated by a society that was much more egotistical and acquisitive. They had seen tremendous changes in their lifetimes, yet now were faced with the unchangeable face of death—prepared for their own death, but utterly debilitated by the death of a child not one, but two generations below them. Crushed with grief but determined to be 'strong' for their grieving, adult child—and then enticed into a group where they should air their inner feelings with this person who knew nothing of the pain they bore within. I offer one of my most heart-wrenching but heart-warming exchanges at the hospice to encourage those who wish to offer support to older generations of grievers. It was with a bereaved grandfather who had clearly struggled at the outset of Cornerstones and was quite antagonistic about my approach. Months later, he told me, 'I thought what you were doing was ill-advised and a waste of time... but I can see now how it has helped our family.'

9

Research with bereaved parents

Infant and childhood mortality rates have declined ten-fold since
1900 (Goldacre, 1983). Survival into adulthood is now an expectation rather than a hope. The experience of child death within a
family is therefore isolating, both socially and emotionally. Death
in childhood is no longer a commonplace event; rather, it is seen
as the failure of modern technology and the scientific age: an unfortunate accident; an embarrassing detour from life's anticipated
route (Cadranell, 1994). Trauma, such as road traffic accidents,
remains the most common cause of childhood death. So many
diseases have been eradicated through vaccine or cure that the
general populace could be forgiven their surprise at the existence
of hospices for children. However, in recent years, given the
widespread publicity required to boost the fundraising needs of
these establishments, their presence and whereabouts have come
to public attention. Children's hospices are nowhere near as prevalent as adult hospices—for the thankful reason that there are far
more deaths in adulthood than in childhood. However, some children, despite our technological advances, are either born with, or
contract, diseases for which there is no cure—and palliative care is
the only option. This is the specialism of the children's hospice,
but the care continues beyond the sad death of a child, with almost all hospices offering continuing bereavement support to the
family. In 1996, Derian House was at the forefront of these initiatives and devised a number of bereavement support approaches
described elsewhere in this book. It is essential, however, that
practice is verified, improved or amended through robust practitioner research. After several years at Derian House and while undertaking post-graduate study, I had the opportunity to conduct a
minor research project with bereaved parents. The children's hospice movement is barely two decades old, so is a particularly un-
der-researched area, although various projects of interest have
been, and are being, undertaken, (Nash, 1999; Robinson and

Jackson, 1999). Following perceived criticism in a Rowntree Foundation report (Robinson and Jackson, 1999), children's hospices were determined to gain and maintain professional respect. The report had, I believe unfairly, implied unsatisfactory standards of care in some children's hospices owing to the 'nursing home' regulations under which these establishments were categorised. In actual fact, the children's hospice movement had expanded so rapidly that statutory regulation was not keeping pace, and no appropriate regulatory body or methodology was then in place. However, service-users—the families of sick and dying children—gave a much more favourable and positive portrayal (Nash, 1999).

After several years of establishing and maintaining the bereavement support service of a children's hospice, the opportunity to conduct some research overwhelmed me with a wealth of topics. There were many areas vying for my attention: gender differences in grief; sibling loss; outcomes for support group participants; support by telephone... Ultimately, the most pressing desire was to examine the linguistics, the narrative, and the context that bereaved parents utilised to discuss their child who had died.

Since my involvement with this uniquely informative and sagacious group of clients, I am aware that I have abdicated any conception of 'expertise'. I endorse the statement of Hindmarch in the preface to the second edition of her thoughtful work, *On the Death of a Child*:

> '*Basic learning has been gained by following the first guiding principle which is advocated for professionals offering support:* **to listen to what individual people say they want rather than presuming what they need.** *The only experts are bereaved family members themselves.*'
>
> (Hindmarch, 2000)

It was to these experts I turned, knowing that the intensity of their illustrations, the articulation of their thought process, the raw honesty of their pain, all combine to offer insights which sometimes endorse, sometimes dispute and sometimes defy 'theories' of grief and bereavement. The aim of the research was to assimilate and examine narrative from bereaved parents in the hope that my own practice would be usefully reinforced and a broader knowledge base established. The continued development of my own practice was increasingly amplified by the voices of bereaved parents themselves.

My endeavour was not necessarily to prove or disprove a particular theory on grief and bereavement. Rather, it was the sincere undertaking of a practitioner wishing to reflect upon, clarify and evaluate her own practice (Wosket, 1999), in the light of responses and narrative from the bereaved client group.

The research question was finally honed into: 'What are the narrative constructs of bereaved parents?' This incorporated the quest for meaning in a family's adaptive, post-bereavement life-journey. A recent addition to the literature (Klass, 1999) had provided an ethnographic study of North American bereaved parents and their process. Narrative had formed a large part of that author's experience and his participatory, non-directional approach closely echoed some of my own intentions with bereaved clients.

> *'I have sought to understand parental bereavement and I have been in many kinds of significant, extended conversations with bereaved parents as they have sought to understand themselves.'*

(Klass, 1999)

While Klass's book title and content refer to the spiritual lives of bereaved parents, he admits:

> *'It is difficult to define spiritual because the word often refers to experiences and realities that are beyond words.'*

(ibid)

This highlights the enigma of practitioner research using narrative processes. How does one put into words that which is beyond words?

Even more relevant to my particular piece of research was the work of Paul Rosenblatt, Professor of Sociology at the University of Minnesota. He had conducted many interviews with bereaved families and had evidenced a depth of understanding in narratives relevant to cultural perspectives. He particularly observed the occasional use of the present tense by bereaved parents in speaking of their deceased child. Rosenblatt asserted that this was rarely indicative of pathological grief (see *Grief Theories* in Section I) or any connotations with denial (Rosenblatt, 2000a; 2000b; 1996).

It did not seem appropriate to analyse the narrative constructs of bereaved parents within the positivist confines of scientific social research. Nor did it seem helpful to employ a technique that rested uncomfortably with the counselling approach I favour. As I operate from a phenomenological standpoint, highlighting an awareness of the client's frame of reference and unique experience, I opted almost inevitably for a qualitative approach through an unstructured interview process. This decision was endorsed by contrast between qualitative and quantitative methodologies (McLeod, 1999), which offered some guidance as to the nature of the researcher as well as the research.

Narrative approaches generally examine the role and significance of stories within counselling and psychotherapy. It is a burgeoning field, sometimes heralded as a 'new' approach—but, of course, 'there is nothing new under the sun' (Ecclesiastes) and the tool of narrative has existed as long as language itself—indeed, perhaps prior to that, as stories unfolded pictorially along cave walls.

My own journey alongside bereaved parents has led me to ponder whether they are in a process of remembering with clarity and forgetting with discernment, as their stories gradually develop into a tolerable segment of their biography. McLeod (1997) proposes an interesting concept when he suggests areas of future research:

> 'To what extent is "improvement" in therapy clients expressed in the ways that they tell their stories, or in the type of stories that they tell? Can stories be used as outcome measures?'

In a more informal sense, the above crystallised the strivings of this particular project: to hear clients' stories a little further down the road and assess their emotional well-being from those stories. My interest in narrative constructs flows naturally from an interest in linguistics and root-words. The Greek word *holos* is the, fairly obvious, root for our words *holistic* and *healing*. Less obviously, *holos* translates as 'putting things in the right order'—an interesting definition of the healing capacity of a narrative approach?

Research plan

The research incorporated samples from an initial population of bereaved parents associated with a children's hospice in the north of England. From the wider population, a stratified group was selected according to the following criteria:

1. Those families who were more than two years post-bereavement;

2. Those families no longer presenting ongoing concerns or implications for further counselling, as assessed by the researcher's previous contact and continuing knowledge of the families;

3. Those families still within a manageable geographical boundary for interviews;

4. Those families who utilised individual and group support interventions (Stepping Stones), thus having prior experience of, and rapport with, the researcher.

An interesting topic for future research would be differentials between those clients utilising the group support intervention and those who declined such assistance. Close consideration was given to including a balanced selection from each in the sample group, but, for this smaller piece of research, the focus upon narrative, linguistics and vocabulary constrained me towards a client-group who evidenced an ability to discuss openly and articulate their experience. This did not preclude variety; rather, it formed part of the focus of the research question and left avenues open for further research as a progression from the initial conclusions.

An initial letter was sent to the twenty-five families who fulfilled the criteria. The letter was not excessively explicit as there was no wish to undermine the spontaneity of subsequent interviews. All families responded by returning their reply slips; twenty-four of those indicated that they would be prepared to participate in a recorded interview. These responses were placed in blank envelopes and a neutral observer made a random selection.

Eight participants (four couples) were selected and informed, with thanks, of their imminent participation. Those families not selected were, naturally, also responded to—with some chagrin at having to decline their willing offers of support in such a sensitive research area.

Ethics

Research involving bereaved parents must inevitably touch on topics of great sensitivity and some pain. There will almost always be an imbalance of power in the counselling relationship and some issues of transference (Wosket, 1999). This is particularly apparent in bereavement counselling where clients are at their most vulnerable and emotionally depleted. The British Association for Counselling and Psychotherapy had published ethical guidelines for monitoring, evaluation and research in counselling (McGuire, 1996), and these were closely adhered to.

The BACP guidelines state:

'The emotional state of the client should be considered; if the client is unlikely to be able to exercise free choice, then they should not be included in the investigation.'

This assessment therefore constituted part of the inclusion criteria.

The ability of bereaved parents to exercise free consent is an area of concern with this particular client group as I am aware of the overtly positive and appreciative bias that tends to be reflected in evaluations of the bereavement support service. Undoubtedly there are often feelings of warmth and gratitude towards those who have remained alongside throughout their client's darkest hours—and an associated reluctance to refuse reciprocal 'help' when requested. For that reason, the initial letter was carefully phrased in order to facilitate refusal for those clients who had no wish to participate in research. Likewise, the reply slip was deliberately kept to a simple;

I/We would/would not be prepared to participate in a recorded interview
(please delete as appropriate)

This eliminated any dilemma on the part of the respondents concerning how to phrase a refusal. Nevertheless, response was 100 per cent with only one respondent declining an offer of participation, which only served to reinforce my concerns. This confirmed my option for unstructured interviews as I felt these, at least, afforded the participants an element of choice, self-monitoring and personal emotional safety.

As suggested by the BACP guidelines, the following strategies were included in the information for participants:

- The purpose of the research
- What participants will be asked to do
- Whether or not their identity will be known to anyone other than the researcher
- What will happen to the written and recorded information
- The right to withdraw consent at any stage.

The selection mode has been addressed previously—those who were selected were assured that they could withdraw consent at any time and have all documentation and audio-information destroyed.

They were also assured that confidentiality and anonymity would be maintained appropriately. Inevitably, participants could easily recognise their own words within this text, but their earnest desire to further understanding of child loss eliminated any concerns about scrupulous anonymity. In fact, the use of anonymity within the text comes from recognised practice in ethical research, rather than from participants themselves. Additionally, counselling or emotional support was in place from another practitioner completely removed from the hospice environment should any of the participants need to avail themselves of it. Clearly, these interviews were to involve former clients in reliving feelings and experiences of potent and poignant impact. The resultant effect upon their emotional equilibrium was, at that stage, an unknown quantity, but one where precautionary measures needed to be in place. I was conscious of holding interviews within the participants' own homes (which could have been perceived as an invasion of their territory), but as I had, in the past, visited each of these homes, I concluded it was not too intrusive.

Throughout the project I received my customary counselling supervision; I also had the facility of academic supervision and an *appropriate, disinterested, external advisor* (McGuire, 1996).

As a scientific investigation, the project is acknowledged to be significantly flawed, in that there was no control group, the researcher was known to the participants, interpretation of data could be subjective, and a clear bias pre-existed in the researcher. This all indicates further recommendations for more extensive research. Notwithstanding the above, the responsibility of interpreting discourse with bereaved parents with as much honesty and balance as possible rested heavily on me. There was an obligation not to distort or adjust (knowingly or unwittingly) such candid disclosures so graciously given. While external, ethical proprieties were in place, the most potent monitor of ethical practice was probably the *internal supervisor* (Casement, 1986), ensuring that my preferred phenomenological approach guaranteed that the interviewee's frame of reference took precedence.

Interviews

The selected couples fell into the following categories:

- They were married couples and none had had previous marriages
- They were between 3 years 2 months, and 4 years post-bereavement

- One couple had lost their only child
- Two couples had two surviving children
- One couple had a surviving child and, subsequently, a new baby
- One couple was on the brink of a (temporary?) emigration
- One couple had moved house since their child's death
- Two couples remained in the homes where their child died
- All were in employment.

Of the deceased children, two were male and two were female, with their ages ranging from 10 months to 18 years.

Even from this outline information, it is clear that, although the participants undoubtedly share commonalities, equally they display wide-ranging differences in their experience of the death of a child and their subsequent lifestyles.

Each interview took place in the home of the interviewees and was to be a minimum of two hours long, although each encounter slightly exceeded that. Three were evening encounters and one was conducted during an afternoon. Interviews were unstructured in the sense that the aim was for parents to reminisce and expand freely upon their past and present. However, each interview did commence with an explanation from the researcher on the nature of the project, and an opening question;

> 'If I were to say, "tell me about" ... (their child who died), where would you start?'

The conversation continued following a direction largely dictated by the parents although, inevitably, the researcher must have influenced that direction when interjecting with queries about visiting the grave, keeping memorabilia, marking anniversaries. Primarily, however, participants were encouraged to pursue their own train of thought.

Each interview was audio-taped using an unobtrusive machine which lay on a low table in the room. Participants were clearly aware of its presence but did not appear to be overly conscious of it.

The person of the researcher

One of the by-products of the research was an awareness of my own feelings in the situation. I had a cerebral knowledge of my inevitable bias and former close involvement with each of the participants, but I was unprepared for the personal feelings this would elicit. When I purposefully and thoughtfully opened the randomly selected envelopes to discover the identity of my prospective interviewees, I was flooded with my own recollections of each participant. I pictured them, recalled the dominant features of their personalities, recalled their involvement in a Stepping Stones programme, recalled their tragic loss—and found myself anticipating with enthusiasm the prospect of an up-dating encounter with them. Clearly, this indicates the preconceptions with which interviews commenced, but equally, my academic curiosity was genuinely prepared to be surprised by what might unfold.

As was apparent from the literature review I had undertaken, my own experience had led me to align myself with the post-modern practice of allowing bereaved parents to find their own route through grief rather than prescribing a set route. I must also acknowledge an affiliation with those authors who endorsed the 'continuing bonds' approach to bereaved parents. In counselling over two hundred bereaved clients, I had not encountered a parent who wished to walk away from their bereavement without a backward glance. While parents might occasionally say, 'I know I have to let go', echoing a more severance-orientated philosophy, I suspect they were primarily adhering to the social constructs prevalent in our society. Bereaved parents were keenly aware of the nuances within a chosen vocabulary, and were greatly relieved to find a counselling response that endorsed their intuitive sense that *moving on* did not have to be synonymous with *leaving their child behind*.

The associate who fulfilled the role of 'appropriate, disinterested and external advisor' (McGuire, 1996) usefully—and critically—commented that the transcribed interviews read more like a bereavement counselling session than a research interview. Initially aghast at my inadequacies, I eventually appreciated that it had, in fact, been my endeavour to facilitate a warmer and more therapeutic encounter rather than a rigid schema of research questions.

The same associate commented that my foreknowledge of these participants had entered into the context of the interviews. My interjections, although comparatively brief, echoed the remembrances of the interviewees at times. This presented an acknowledged dilemma, for I could not *pretend* that I was hearing their story for the first time—nor, indeed, imply that I had forgotten all our previous encounters. That would defy the congruence that was a central facet to my counselling approach. I could only present this as a perspective on the subsequent analysis and results and ponder, as previously, the outcomes if a stranger to the families had conducted the interviews. I cannot deny I am involved with this topic but, equally, that involvement may have opened up conversations that would have been unlikely in another environment. Conversely, my approach with these families at the time of their loss may have influenced their journey through grief. Had I been an adherent to the 'resolution' and 'closure' philosophies, would that have been reflected in the responses of my clients? Clearly this was an area that could only be clarified through further and wider research.

Data analysis

The ensuing reams of text were labouriously transcribed, a task I undertook personally, not only for confidentiality, but also to immerse myself more thoroughly in the memoirs. I could associate the words with nuances of gesture, expression or body language that had featured, glances between couples; but transcription also offered the retrospective opportunity to hear the participants more fully, both aurally and cognitively, for the plethora of words and thoughts in the interview had been impossible to absorb in their entirety at the time. As intended, the content of the conversation was principally the words of the parents; for example, the transcription of one exchange culminated in 225 statements attributable to the parents, with 13 queries from the researcher.

A Theme-Analysis approach was applied (Meier and Boivin, 2000) not only in accordance with anticipated themes, but crediting specifically the material that arose within the exchanges.

Within the dual interpretation of *construct*, that is, a group of words forming a phrase, or, the meaning inherent in a phrase, portions of text were categorised and accorded to one of three themes that had emerged from the encounters.

> *'The aim of open coding is to discover, name and categorise phenomena; also to develop categories in terms of their properties and dimensions.'*
>
> (Strauss and Corbin, 1990: 181)

Thematic identification was undertaken through the use of colour-coding, a simple but effective method whereby the transcripts became a vivid representation of the following themes:

- Connectedness (holding on)

- Severance (letting go)

- Spirituality (religious faith and/or supernatural experiences).

These themes evolved from the original material and a series of word or phrase searches. To fully capture the meanings within these particular narratives it was necessary to read the transcripts repeatedly until an intuitive sense of the locus of the participant became clear.

Qualitative research is chiefly concerned with meanings: patterns of behaviour and the way people understand things. This relies upon clarity, authenticity and integrity in the interpretation, but also elements of self-confidence: 'to what extent am I willing to trust my own interpretation of an interview transcript?' (McLeod, 1999).

So for the purpose of analysis, it should be clarified that the meanings behind the three category headings were defined as:

- *Connectedness*: those statements or phrases that referred to the continuing presence of their dead child in the thoughts and actions of the speaker

- *Severance*: those statements or phrases that referred to a detachment, or movement away from their dead child in the thoughts and actions of the speaker

- *Spirituality*: those statements or phrases that referred to either a religious faith or some supernatural connection with their child who died.

Only phrases, not individual words, were selected, as removing single words out of context from the narrative could rapidly lead to misinterpretation.

In addition to the three main categories, various commonalities presented themselves from the data and these will be discussed subsequently.

The participating couples were referred to as Male a – d and Female a – d.

References to:

	Connect- edness	Severance	Spirituality
Male and female a:	63	9	1
Male and female b:	39	7	8
Male and female c:	41	13	6
Male and female d:	75	11	7

From these 280 responses, it can be noted that references to connectedness constituted 78 per cent of the sample, severance 14 per cent, and spirituality 8 per cent.

This is not a precise science as references could quite easily overlap—and certainly the spiritual references could be deemed to belong with either connectedness or severance. For the purpose of this undertaking, however, the intention was to select those phrases that could be clearly delineated into a category.

The majority of statements referring to their deceased child were in the past tense, with the occasional lapse into present, or a deliberate use of the present tense when responding to the query, 'How many children do you tell people you have?' (All participants included their child who had died in their response.)

Although the interviews were unstructured, there were similar areas covered in each one—either brought into the narrative by the parents or focused by the researcher, as in the above question. Other queries included:

'Do you visit the grave?'

and

'Do you carry any memorabilia with you?'

Interestingly, three of the eight (two females and one male) carried remembrance items with them at all times.

Laughter featured in each encounter, but tears only surfaced in one.

On conclusion, and unbidden, each participant commented that it had been 'good' to talk about their child.

My style of working with clients was reflected in my approach to analysing research data. I followed, rather than led, a client, trusting their innate ability to highlight their most pressing issues for themselves. Similarly, my hope was that recorded interviews would suggest their own themes and structures. I had no fixed preconception as to which themes would emerge, although the three categories highlighted are all of interest to me.

'Generally... unstructured interviews have as their aim "discovery" rather than "checking". They lend themselves to in-depth investigations, particularly those which explore personal accounts of experiences and feelings.'
(Denscombe, 1998)

Through reflective reading and re-reading, themes and interconnections emerged, not necessarily instigated by the research questions. For example, each family mentioned photographs and videos, a topic that was never introduced by the researcher.

Research on a topic so closely affiliated to my everyday working role was always going to be empirical. The experience of interacting with bereaved families continued to inform my practice.

Findings

More generalised findings will be discussed prior to a closer examination of the three categories highlighted in the thematic indexing. Some direct quotations from interview transcripts will be incorporated. Significantly, a family I contacted to enquire about changing their child's name in a quotation, for the sake of confidentiality, did not want her name altered. Even in quotations, she continues to exist as an important member of their household. Several phenomena arose that were not necessarily themes, although they may have occurred repeatedly in different interviews, thus emphasising their significance. Eight of these phenomena will be addressed individually.

Pragmatism

Bereaved families appeared to have a radically altered perspective on life. Priorities had been re-established, particularly with regard to materialism. Having experienced the worst loss a parent can experience, the temporal trappings of life were reduced in their significance. One mother commented that if a colleague was anxious about their cat, she felt frustrated by the apparent trivia of other people's lives. Another commented on the lack of sensitivity in her workplace, not just for her own situation, but ongoing insensitivity generally—although she acknowledged that it was the death of her child that had heightened her awareness of it, musing '*I suppose I was like that before.*'

One family had moved house and discovered that the pain of leaving the house where their child had lived and died was mollified by the realisation that her presence was not reliant upon bricks and mortar, but on their own internal narrative. '*Even if we burnt every single memento we had of hers, it wouldn't make a jot of difference to our relationship as it stands with her now. It wouldn't.*'

The unpredictability of life had become a stark reality for them. For those whose lives have been untainted by tragedy, perhaps ignorance is bliss and long-term plans could be sketched out with impunity. For these parents, forward planning had taken on a new trepidation. Even in the course of their grieving, there was an acknowledgement of an unknown future, although some internalised certainties prevailed: '*I know I will never not hurt, that depth of pain will always be there.*' Yet other musings, such as the length of time they would visit a grave, include the child's name on family cards, attend memorial services, were greeted with the philosophical stance of '*we'll cross that bridge when we come to it*'.

Career changes

Linked with their changed perspectives, it is interesting to note that five of the eight participants had changed career since the death of their child. For two of the mothers this constituted a return to the workplace that would have been impossible while their child was alive. However, the other three had made deliberate and life-affecting changes. Of the three who remained with their former careers, two expressed immense dissatisfaction with their working life and longed to find something '*more fulfilling*'. Consequently, only one of the eight was satisfied with the career path they had chosen some years previously. This is not only a reflection of the disorientation and restlessness associated with child loss, but also reaffirms the changed priorities, perspectives and philosophies referred to earlier. One couple had boldly named a new business venture after their child—with the double-edged sword of the constant use of the child's name (which they were pleased with), but the anxiety of the business not succeeding and thereby '*letting her down*' (which they feared). It was, for them, a significant, although precarious, memorial to their child. '*I think that's my biggest fear, that people will forget her. I know she's only mine but I want everyone to remember her.*'

The grave

One family did not have a grave *per se*, simply a significant place where their child's ashes are interred, which they visit very occasionally. Remarkably, the same family had a profound and active religious faith and it is their assurance of their child's presence '*in Heaven*' that marks their relative indifference to earthly monuments.

Of the other three couples, two had very differing feelings, between partners, about visiting the grave and one couple both visited the grave infrequently. Of the two couples where one visited the grave regularly while their partner found it meaningless, one visitor was male and one, female—thus eliminating any precept, in this particular sample, that a gender issue may have been highlighted.

Within one couple, one partner could say, *'that's where I can talk to him'*, while the other responded, *'I just don't see him there'*; very different attitudes but announced without fear of criticism or disapproval from their partner. This is a notable indicator of the individuation that can occur within bereaved parents' relationships—a topic to be addressed in more detail later.

One mother, who visited her child's grave but felt no obligation to attend with ritualistic regularity, commented that spending time with their child's body prior to the funeral had confirmed for the parents the comparative insignificance of the 'shell' of their child: *'the more we went, the less she was Rachael.'* Such a perception was a sustaining preparation for their child's funeral,

Similarly, a comment was made: *'You could go to the grave every day... or you could go once every year—it doesn't matter y'know, it's what's in here* [hand on heart] *that counts.'*

Number of children

Each participant was asked how they respond when asked how many children they have. As mentioned earlier, all participants favoured including their child who had died in any such response. There were, however, occasions where parents had simplified the response for the sake of rescuing the questioner, perhaps in a very superficial encounter where a lengthy explanation might be inappropriate or painful at that particular time. *'I still want to say I've got three children, I don't want to say I've got two children. I do, sometimes—ust because I can't... it's simpler—but I don't want to. Every time I do it I feel like I'm letting him down.'*

In other interactions and conversations, there was a growing reluctance to share their history with other people, which belied the bereaved parents' wistful urge to tell their story. *'I wanted to tell people, but I find it hard to tell people because a lot of people aren't interested in your life.'* A sad indictment of how story-telling and listening have lapsed in our society where speed is of the essence, where a facile enquiry after another's well-being is proffered without any slowing of step so that any answer remains unheard—and often, despairingly, unspoken.

Memorabilia

This constituted a large part of each interview. Each family had photographs on display, although there were mixed responses in their ability to watch videos of their child. Three of the couples had albums chronicling their child's life, the preparation of which had been in itself therapeutic, although costly. *'They were good things to do though, even though they're painful.'* All families had stored precious items associated with their child, and these included condolence cards, which were safely stored but not frequently read. One mother had still not read all the cards received three and a half years after her child's death, but she was satisfied that they were safely stored. Most families had a specific *memory box* in which they kept this treasured memorabilia. One father had designed and made the box himself, with the aid of the child's surviving siblings, and he commented, with some perplexity, *'I know I enjoyed doing it.'*

Three of those interviewed carried a remembrance item with them at all times. One mother, touchingly, wore a medallion identical to one her child was buried with, bearing the inscription 'Lord, keep us together while we are apart.'

One couple commented that, while they had a lock of hair on continuous display with a photograph, the incidental discovery of another lock of hair in a box—one which they could touch and smell—brought forth a sudden, irrepressible, tearful emotional response. *'It was just that I got a whiff of her y'know, and it was just so…bliss. A hard bliss.'*

Associative items, photographs, letters, documentation, clothing—all were intrinsic elements to the reminiscences of parents—although with the astute awareness that most memorabilia did not retain the same potent significance that it may have had in times of very recent bereavement. For example, each family had been able to change their child's bedroom, to a greater or lesser extent. In fact, each had changed the function of the room, with only those parents who lost their only child maintaining the original décor and items on display, and despite the room now having a dual function.

(To interject: from a wider experience of bereaved families, I note that there are those who have no desire, and see no necessity, to alter their child's room. Frequently, this is where the household has no other pressing need for the practicality of additional space or another room. I would not necessarily assess this choice as indicating pathologised grief, rather an alternative adaptive response. The room itself becomes the *memory box*.)

Each family marked the anniversaries of their child's birthday and death date with specific acts of remembrance, and felt that these, and other specific dates, were never likely to pass unacknowledged.

Tears

Each interview undoubtedly held emotive content. The narrative was interspersed with pauses and hesitancy at times, which reflected the allegiance to a therapeutic approach rather than one that was more prescriptive and formulaic. It was necessary to allow interviewees their silences and thoughtful moments in the course of the encounter and an unhurried atmosphere was paramount in the circumstances.

In much earlier interventions of bereavement support with these families, tears were a not uncommon feature. During the research interviews, only two participants shed tears, although, at times, they were clearly not far from the surface for other participants. I was led to reflect how poor an indicator tears are of the emotional status of a person. By my assessment, the two who shed tears were particularly well-adjusted and accepting of their roller-coaster emotions, whereas another of the sample group was clearly depressed and too deflated to cry.

There was also a stated ability to control situations or make personal choices about opportunities for disclosure or strategic non-disclosure, depending on how fragile or sturdy they felt at any given time: '*You find yourself pulling back.*'

Laughter

Laughter featured more prominently in the encounters than tears, although in various guises:

- *Genuine amusement*: anecdotes were shared that invariably raise a smile despite their poignancy
- *Self-deprecation*: the slightly embarrassed laughter around revealing a perceived fallibility
- *Defensive laughter*: the mechanism that sometimes succeeds in keeping the tears at bay
- *Restorative laughter*: the gleeful pronouncement of one's self-esteem and strength in still being able to maintain an enigmatically light-hearted outlook on life.

Laughter is such a powerful tool in our linguistic repertoire; unique to humans, and a fascinating research topic in its own right. Humour is a key concept within British society and does not necessarily translate accurately to other cultures. Laughter can probably be as offensive as it can be unifying. I recall much laughter through the Stepping Stones programme, occasioned by the relief of bereaved parents sharing an evening with other bereaved parents, unhampered by the guilt that so often beset them if they were observed laughing in a public place. The psychologist Dorothy Rowe suggests:

> 'We all need to capture and hold on to laughter. Humour reduces people and events to an appropriate size. Whenever we feel that our meaning structure is threatened, laughter reduces the threat to manageable proportions and strengthens our self-confidence, even as we admit our weakness.'
>
> (Rowe, 2000)

Individual differences

One of the most striking and surprising elements for me, in my capacity as 'former' bereavement counsellor to these families, was the growth in tolerance that had evolved between the two partners in a relationship. I was fully aware of earlier, classic frustrations in relationships where one partner grieved in a very different manner from the other. I would like to imagine their new found acceptance was a result of my earlier interventions with them, but I suspect it is more likely the case that the tender and raw wounds of early grief are not as exposed and an ability to rationalise has returned.

Certainly, major differences in outlook, actions and abilities were manifest in each partnership. Paradoxically, there was a tangible closeness and comfortable security within each of the relationships.

Quite radical individual differences were greeted with smiles, expressive eye contact and tolerance, as if the intervening years had brought an awareness of their individuality that made them more durable as a couple.

Emergent themes

The three themes mentioned earlier will be considered in more detail.

Connectedness

The last decade has heralded progressive developments in bereavement theory where practitioners and theorists have acknowledged the uniqueness of each client's story. The search for an ideal therapeutic procedure may thus be self-limiting as, ultimately, individual approaches to each different client will predominate.

> 'This would require a highly sensitive receptivity—an open listening to the client voice, for the reality and values of its sustaining subculture.'
>
> (Stroebe et al, 1992)

Despite this welcomed individuation of clients, *listening to the client voice* has also revealed commonalities and themes that are so pervasive it would seem imprudent to ignore them.

Foremost amongst these is the theme of connectedness. In the fullness of time, historians and social analysts may cite a relatively brief period—perhaps from late-Victorian to post-modern times—where British society favoured conclusive styles of grieving, which advocated detachment and completion. We commence a new millennium with new thinking permeating society; a slow process, but one that is undoubtedly underway. Spearheading these changes will be bereaved families themselves who have been emboldened (with the support of recent theorists) to tell their stories more accurately than ever before. Parents now dare to proclaim about the child they lost:

> *'Whatever we do, we don't have to go through rituals to make her close to us.'*

> *'You don't get over it, you just get different ways of dealing with it.'*

> *'Wherever I am, he is, and I think that's how I cope.'*

They carry their key-rings, wear their lockets and defiantly state the numbers in their family, including the child who died. This is what will impact a society who, by and large, are unlikely to read many handbooks on bereavement theory.

In interviews with bereaved parents, the overwhelming impression I departed with on each occasion was of the inclusive sense of their child in the family. A mother who had subsequently had another baby, had clutched, throughout her labour and delivery, a small, silver-framed photo of their child who died. They were satisfied that the whole family had been present at the birth and in the quiet moments when mother and new baby were alone, she introduced the siblings to each other—one brand new and the other sadly missed but ever present. *'That's how I dealt with it,'* she said, simply.

Those are the stories that will enlighten society. Having subsequent children after a bereavement is not about filling gaps as if a family were a supermarket shelf, it is about continuing as a family and maintaining every child's position in that family.

This ability to maintain connections would appear to increase rather than diminish in the course of grief. Actually, much of the distress of the early, traumatic months after bereavement is focused on an inability to visualise their child or, perhaps only visualise final, distressing moments or a period of sickness.

d parentsBereaved parents may panic that they have forgotten the sound of their child's voice... And yet, some months later, be convinced they heard that self-same voice in another room.

The emotional turmoil of recent, raw grief leaves scant capacity for the bereaved parent to accommodate the inner representation of their dead child. Hence, a powerful attachment to external memorials and people who knew their child. A bereaved mother, referring to memories, said: '*You're afraid... they fade and then... when they've stopped fading they come back even stronger.*'

Perhaps the willingness to participate in research interviews is, of itself, a refection of bereaved parents' insistence on maintaining links with their child.

'*The end of grief is not severing the bond with a dead child, but integrating the child into the parent's life in a different way than when the child was alive. Phenomena that indicate interactions with the dead child change from being mysterious to being an everyday part of life.*'

(Klass *et al*, 1996)

Severance

The term seems very stark now, in the light of previous comments, but occasional reference was made to a kind of detachment. Some were comments that fulfilled the social norm, such as, '*we're getting on with life now, aren't we?*'

Other indications of transition may be perceived to have elements of severance in them, like changing a bedroom, visiting a grave less frequently, putting items away in a box. One bereaved father used the same analogy for his thoughts and emotions: '*At times, I've got to sort of use my head instead of my emotions, otherwise it will become very destructive... you're sort of pushing it back, y'know, back in its little box.*'

One mother stated, '*I can accept that he's gone,*' then, to her husband asked, '*but you can't let him go, can you?*'

Another family commented that the first anniversary of their child's death had been something of a milestone and left them '*feeling we've got to move forward in the best way we can.*'

Klass (1999) comments that the process of mourning might best be conceived as an interplay between integration and dissociation. That being so, dissociation might have been a more appropriate word than severance. It could also replace the hackneyed descriptions of denial and avoidance. Grief itself manifests non-denial.

Use of the word 'severance' gives a stark comparison with amputation. Acute pain; a healing period interspersed with phantom pains from a limb that no longer exists but is well remembered by neurological pathways; and an adoption of strategies to integrate the loss into active life.

Elements of severance will inevitably constitute part of the grieving for bereaved parents, but rarely overwhelm the predominant feelings of connectedness. One bereaved father summarised the curious interaction between dissociation and integration when he said, '*Though I've not—what's termed as—"let go", I feel I can "not let go" but still use it to advantage.*'

Spirituality

This unexpected addition to the themes materialised out of the realisation that each family had introduced, completely unbidden, an element of spirituality into the conversations.

Only one family found an enduring commitment to a Christian faith sustaining, and it was notable that this family made only one overt reference to spirituality—and that was in the context of another family's child being '*in Heaven longer than she'd been on earth.*' The limited explicit statements probably indicated the internalised constancy of their unshakeable structures of faith, inherent in their daily living.

Another bereaved father, who had previously had a vibrant Christian faith, still believed his son was safe in Heaven, but now had the conflict of requiring '*more proof*' than previously.

An urge to be assured of their child's ongoing existence in eternity is a common—and understandable—occurrence for bereaved parents. A perennial dilemma; there are those who would not countenance visiting clairvoyants or spiritualists; there are those who may visit only to be bitterly disappointed; those who may visit, hear a *message* and feel more frustrated than ever; and those who are satisfied with reassurances of their child's ongoing existence. Rare are the bereaved parents who do not feel their child continues in *any form*, including those of various faiths or none.

One bereaved mother had an unexpected and unplanned encounter with a tarot reader who commented that she could 'see' a little girl at the mother's side continually. The disconcerted but curiously comforted mother told me, *'I thought, well, that's a nice idea and if it was true it would be nice to sort of think of it that way.'*

Several references were made to a deceased child being like a guardian angel, 'looking down' on them and 'protecting' them. Parents whose days were previously spent nurturing and protecting their child, now feel themselves to be the recipients of a mystical protection that is constantly with them. For some, the metaphysical and the spiritual become intertwined.

Conclusions and implications for practice

The experience of in-depth discussion with longer-term bereaved parents was illuminating and reassuring. The theory of ongoing connectedness with a loved one who dies—but most particularly, a child—had been endorsed. As mentioned at the outset, the intention of this endeavour was not necessarily to prove or disprove a theory, but to validate, or amend, my own therapeutic counselling stance. I recognised the apparent importance of ongoing connectedness with their child to bereaved parents, and I felt that was affirmed in the data. Throughout interviews, there was an overwhelming sense of an unshakeable bond between parent and child. An impression equally authenticated by my external associate.

In the course of undertaking the project, an article by a bereaved mother appeared in a national newspaper. The mother was recounting her frustration with the taboo of acknowledging child death. Specifically, she resented the implication that she should have got over the death of her firstborn baby ten years previously, especially as she now had three healthy children.

'People often comment on the children… and there are times when it seems necessary, to me, to point out that I have actually had four children.'

(Kettleborough, 2000)

She goes on to say:

'The point has been made many times that there is no word in our vocabulary for bereaved parents. We have orphans, widows and widowers, yet bereaved parents are not catered for in our language. Our situation appears unacknowledged. It is too dreadful for many people even to comprehend.'

The expedient use of narrative as an intervention with bereaved parents has been emphasised, as has the parents' ability to cognitively restructure their environment through that narrative. It is an area for further research and certainly presented me with further contemplation:

- Would the inability to articulate their grief into narrative be a preventive for some?

- Will an ever-changing narrative result in a distancing from truth?

- Are the constructs within a narrative societal, cultural or personal?

- Is narrative equally important for bereaved children?—or is that where we stole it from anyway?

I felt the overwhelming intimation in bereaved parents' conversation was towards ongoing connectedness with their deceased child. This also concurred with my personal precept of the grief process as cyclical rather than linear. This is, of course, not an entirely new concept; CS Lewis identified it in his own grief some years earlier:

'Tonight all the hells of young grief have opened again; the mad words, the bitter resentment, the fluttering in the stomach, the nightmare unreality, the wallowed-in tears. For in grief nothing "stays put". One keeps on emerging from a phase, but

it always recurs. Round and round. Everything repeats. Am I going in circles, or dare I hope I am on a spiral? But if a spiral am I going up or down it?'

(Neuberger, 1999)

References

Cadranell J (1994) Talking about death—parents and children. In: Hill L, ed. *Caring for Dying Children and their Families*. Chapman and Hall, London

Casement P (1986) *On Learning from the Patient*. Tavistock Publications, London

Denscombe M (1998) *The Good Research Guide*. Open University Press, Buckingham

Goldacre MJ (1983) Health and sickness in the community. In: Weatherall D, Ledingham J, Worrell D, eds. *Oxford Textbook of Medicine*, Vol. 1. Oxford University Press, New York

Hindmarch C (2000) *On the Death of a Child*. Radcliffe Medical Press, Oxford

Kettleborough J (2000) In: *Mail on Sunday*, 2.07.00, London

Klass D (1999) *The Spiritual Lives of Bereaved Parents*. Taylor and Francis, Philadelphia

Klass D, Silverman P, Nickman S (1996) *Continuing Bonds*. Taylor and Francis, Washington, DC

McGuire A (1996) *Ethical Guidelines for Monitoring, Evaluation and Reserch in Counselling*. BAC, Rugby

McLeod J (1999) *Practitioner Research in Counselling*. Sage, London

McLeod J (1997) *Narrative and Psychotherapy*. Sage, London

Meier A, Boivin M (2000) Narrative in psychotherapy theory, practice and research: a critical review. *Psychother Res* **10**: 57–77

Nash T (1999) A children's hospice: a place for living. In: *Children and Death 4th International Conference*, Bristol UK

Neuberger J (1999) *Dying Well*. Hochland and Hochland, Cheshire

Robinson C, Jackson P (1999) *Children's Hospices: Lifeline for Families?* Joseph Rowntree Foundation, NCB, London

Rosenblatt PC (2000a) *Parent Grief: Narratives of Loss and Relationship*. Brunner/Mazel, Philadelphia

Rosenblatt PC (2000b) Parents talking in the present tense about their dead child. *Bereavement Care* **19**: 35–38

Rosenblatt PC (1996) Grief that does not end. In: Klass D, Silverman P, Nickman S, eds. *Continuing Bonds*. Taylor and Francis, Philadelphia

Rowe D (2000) *Friends and Enemies*. Harper Collins, London

Strauss A, Corbin J (1990) *Grounded Theory Procedures and Techniques*. Sage, London

Stroebe M, Gergen M, Gergen K, Stroebe W (1992) Broken hearts or broken bonds. *Am Psychol* **47**: 1205–12

Wosket V (1999) *The Therapeutic Use of Self*. Routledge, London

Section III

Personal Reflections

10

A personal perspective

There are those who would assert that counselling, as a profession, has evolved out of people's inability, generally, to listen to one another anymore. There may be some truth in that as Western society has accustomed itself to purchasing human services like commodities from a supermarket shelf. We live in an age of instant gratification where food, drink and entertainment are available at the flick of a switch, communication systems have increased speed beyond the imaginings of former generations, and services that fail to fulfil their promise of haste have complaint procedures in place for their disgruntled customers. Consequently, the pace of life is such that the protracted and convoluted route through grief is inconceivable to those who have not experienced it. Perhaps it is a sad indictment of our society that we require models, paradigms and theories of grief in order to support those who are bereaved. It then becomes too easy to categorise grievers and lose sight of our ignorance of each person's individual story. We cannot assume we know its narrative until it has been told to us—and the imperative is to hear each story afresh, without assumptions or predictions. But will we have the time to listen?

Farrell speaks of 'the arrogance of cynicism' where the multiplicity of professionals' and practitioners' experience presents the risk of overlooking the lonely and painfully unique journey of each family living under the shadow of a child's terminal prognosis (Farrell, 1999). There may be an insidious defence mechanism at work that encourages people to propagate models of grief in order to conceal the basic fact that the death of a child is unbearably sad. There is an innate feeling of helplessness within those who accompany grieving parents and siblings on their journey and this can be disconcertingly de-skilling. It is also potently emotive, with a resultant inclination within society to avoid or reject those whose grief we cannot tolerate. Regularly, those who work within the hospice movement—especially children's hospices—are informed by acquaintances, 'I couldn't do *your* job', with the implication that the speaker is far too tender and sensitive to cope with such sadness. The inference, of course, silent or spoken, is that those who choose to work alongside dying children and their families must be hardened and cynical. My experience is that the reverse is true. Those who practise within that environment have chosen to expose their humanity, knowing the cost, but determining to offer their skills at a time and place of great need. For myself, the rewards far exceeded any emotional cost to me. Occasional tears were a small price to pay for the enriching encounters with families who taught so much about existing alongside death and loss. With a Jungian perspective on the shadow or darker, more negative elements of existence, there comes a realisation that all aspects of life make up the whole person. In owning one's shadow experiences, one is not less of a person, but more complete, (Kuykendall, 1998).

Within children's hospice, the potency of existing at the stark interface between life and death is not lost on either carers or those cared for. The years spent in that environment undoubtedly caused me to reflect regularly on life and death, despair and hope, arbitrariness and meaning. As an advocate of reflective practice, I devised a series of questions for self-assessment and self-awareness which, when responded to in a considered and authentic manner, could illuminate a practitioner's attitudinal stance and inform or modify their ongoing practice:

- What are my own thoughts and feelings about death?

- How do I think about/rationalise/come to terms with a child's death?

- How does my attitude affect my way of helping a bereaved family?

- How do I use the person that I am, to best support a family at a difficult time?

- What is the most difficult bereavement support task I could be asked to do?

Simple questions, but profound in their inner searching for the discerning practitioner, requiring honest self-reflection and a truthful recognition of strengths and weaknesses. My own response to the last question would be the role of overseeing the final transference of a child who had died, from bed to coffin. Many parents would want to perform this incredibly poignant and concluding task themselves, but others felt, understandably, it was not an occasion they wanted to be present for. Nevertheless, they preferred someone familiar to be in attendance, and a likely choice would be a member of the hospice staff. On those occasions, I would feel the burden of being *in loco parentis*, yet strangely privileged but humbled to be the last one to see that child's face. It was a duty that certainly carried an emotional cost, but it was also one that I would never have declined.

It would seem highly unlikely to be able to work in a children's hospice without casting some reflection upon the meaning of life. For parents bereaved of a child, life's journey has taken a major diversion and may never return to the planned route. To have the natural order of birth, death and succession overturned leaves bereaved families isolated and disorientated. In addition to the pain of loss, individuals are compelled to try to make sense of the spiritual chaos that ensues.

Spirituality has become an overused, and thereby much abused, concept in recent times, encompassing everything from traditional religious faiths to atheism, from crystals to clairvoyance. Humankind's 'search for meaning' (Frankl, 1987) continues unabated but seems to diverge rather than converge. Enlightenment has done little to concentrate our understanding; rather we have developed the capacity to illuminate more and more of the landscape of spiritual enquiry and discovery, constantly expanding the breadth of our investigation. Current understanding of the term 'spirituality' encompasses the lifelong journey towards meaning, which, for some, will incorporate religious beliefs or faith. When the evanescence of life is acknowledged, there is often an accompanying curiosity about before and afterwards. Spirituality has become an acceptable area of investigation and features widely in the mission statements of organisations that wish to amplify their holistic concern for employees and service-users. Given this fairly wholesale acceptance of the spiritual dimension to individuals, the atheist's journey is no less spiritual than the Muslim's, the Christian's or the Buddhist's. Those with a faith framework may be better equipped to articulate and develop their spirituality, but many with a secular spirituality discover their own expressions of hope and defiance in the face of death.

There may be those critics of the personalisation of funeral services, where relevant modern music takes the place of more formal church music, but the structure of society is changing and the astute cleric would be well advised to adapt and accommodate a generation whose spirituality will increasingly be informed by the media more than the church. Children's funerals particularly become more meaningful for grieving families with the inclusion of readings and songs that carry a personal association for that child. I have been present at funerals where popular music, nursery rhymes or cartoon characters have featured appropriately within the more formal structures of a sad farewell. From Robbie Williams singing *Angels* to Barney the purple dinosaur singing *Just Imagine*, these occasions deserve to be devised by families more than a remote member of the clergy. Those religious ministers, of all faiths, who can demonstrate empathic tolerance to families in distress are far more likely to offer hope and spiritual sustenance to a grieving family than those who rigidly insist upon dogmatic adherence to a timeworn formula. There is also an evolving trend towards having cremation or burial *prior* to a 'celebration of a life' service—which does seem an innately plausible order, giving families the opportunity to conclude the ritual with positive affirmations of their child's existence.

Interestingly, much of current popular music reflects thoughts on life's meaning, limitation or poignancy. Some lyrics, from an American band—The Flaming Lips—carry a surprisingly wistful allusion to both the brevity of an individual's existence and the cyclical continuity of life.

Do you realise, that you have the most beautiful face?
Do you realise, we're floating in space?
Do you realise, that happiness makes you cry?
Do you realise, that everyone you know someday will die?
So instead of saying all of your goodbyes

Let them know you realise that life goes fast,
It's hard to make the good things last,
You realise the sun doesn't go down—
It's just an illusion caused by the world spinning round.
(Reprinted by permission: The Flaming Lips and Scott Booker)

The hospice movement in the UK was innovated and inspired from the Christian perspective of accompanying the dying on their physical and spiritual journey. While acknowledging that death is indiscriminate and ubiquitous, and the hospice movement embraces those of all faiths or none, perhaps there is a place for reflecting on some of the Christian basics upon which the movement was founded. St Columba's Fellowship is an organisation that affirms a Christian presence within the hospice movement, but does so with programmes and conferences that inform and enhance evidence-based practice, as well as offering spiritual refreshment to practitioners.

My own philosophy on life is informed by a Christian faith that pervades my existence and will inevitably colour my perceptions of situations and events. While not necessarily a stance I could or should share with bereaved families, belief in an eternity for all these children certainly bolstered my own sanity and survival in the realm of child death. Despite that, I have been faced on many occasions with circumstances for which I had no explanation or solution. I have discovered that it is possible to be profoundly perplexed without being hopeless. Hope is a quality that stirs the human spirit. Hopelessness and insignificance are two of the most despondent feelings in human existence, and the hospice movement is charged with maintaining hope in unlikely circumstances. Spirituality need not necessarily diminish as physicality wanes. Hope for cure need not be replaced by a gaping void, but by changing hopes; hope for respect, peace, companionship, comfort, significance. Hospice care is not, and never has been, purely about meeting physical needs, but about asking children and families how they are—and lingering long enough to hear the answer.

Patients' hopes:

- That their life has had meaning
- Control of symptoms, especially pain
- To be accepted/loved/respected for the person they are
- To mean something to someone else
- To have decisions and desires considered respectfully
- To prepare for death and life after death (for those left, and for themselves)
- Those facing terminal illness may also use denial at times as a survival mechanism in stressful times. This type of defensive denial can be useful and need not be discouraged; neither should it be reinforced.

What hinders hope?

- Abandonment, isolation, being 'left'. Friends and family who are emotionally distant, although physically present, can exacerbate feelings of rejection
- Differing hopes between family members. Prioritisation should commence, where possible, with the wishes and feelings of the one who is dying
- Lack of recognition for each person's individuality
- Exclusion—openness and honesty are instrumental to creating an atmosphere of trust and security. Hope cannot be engendered in an environment of ambiguity.

The changing face of hope:

- Many families have to accommodate a dawning realisation that hopes of recovery are tenuous, then gone
- Finding ways of living with dying
- Daring to face the sadness, anger, guilt, resentment or a myriad of other emotions that may arise
- Endeavouring to be honest with each other

- Taking time to look back, to appreciate the present—and, maybe, consider the future.

Bereaved parents vigorously and rightly refute any concept that their child's life had no meaning. The fear of many bereaved parents is that their child will be forgotten. The significance of a life—of whatever length—has to be endorsed. Parents need to know that their child's life was 'not for nothing'.

Certainly, those lives were 'not for nothing' when I hear the words of bereaved parents, so distinctively informed by, and interwoven with, the life of their child. A bereaved mother explained her dilemma in trying to support some friends who were on the brink of losing their own child and commencing a journey of grieving similar to the one this mother had traversed some years before:

> *'If I spoke with the family now, who are about to lose their child, it would be as if we were stood on one side of the Grand Canyon and I was telling them they would have to get to the other side. Of course, the leap seems impossible to them and, naturally, it is. What they will never understand or believe, in advance of experiencing it, is that they must struggle down to the very bottom of the canyon, make their way across, then climb laboriously up the other side. But today, they cannot imagine how they would ever accomplish that.'*

Only a bereaved parent can describe that endeavour so succinctly; yet, even they appreciate the incomprehensibility of the task ahead to the newly bereaved.

Another mother allowed me to use some words she wrote, and read, for the placing of her daughter's headstone:

> *Every day a mother loses a daughter,*
> *a father loses the apple of his eye,*
> *brothers, sisters and friends lose someone they love,*
> *but somehow the world still turns.*
>
> *The wonder of what ifs, the buts, the maybes.*
> *The questions that will, and can, never be answered*
> *are always on our minds.*

Hours, days and months go by,
but there isn't one of those days that we don't think of you,
your courage, your determination and your will to live.
There isn't one of those days that we don't miss you,
miss your laugh, your touch, your being.

Some days are so hard the heartache almost consumes me.
Other times we survive day by day,
the world somehow still turning.

The world does indeed keep turning and this task of completing the grave had taken the child's parents more than three years to accomplish, carrying as it did, an emotional burden of finality, realisation and acceptance. Even in writing those words, I am reminded that this mother was not alone in stating that *acceptance* was a point she would never reach, no matter how many textbooks told her otherwise. Acceptance carries with it connotations of resigned acquiescence, but for the parent who has lost a child, it will *never be right*. One of the first truisms I learned from bereaved parents at the hospice was that 'you never get over it—you just get used to it.' The death of a child contravenes the laws of nature and the expectations of parents, but the prematurity of its end does nothing to invalidate a life's meaning.

It was my conviction that no life is meaningless that instigated these writings. '*Life's rich tapestry*' has become a hackneyed phrase imbued with cynicism, yet I regularly return to it for the reassuring analogy that the tiniest stitch may well be more noted by its absence than its presence. A life lived, however briefly, must have produced consequences that would not have been there without that life. There is an interconnectedness to humanity that may be seldom acknowledged, but is nevertheless an unavoidable facet of our existence.

The world turns and life goes on—but that should never be intended as a tired platitude that dismisses the reality and the cost of mourning. Rather, it declares that each life has made its contribution to creation and every life carries its singular significance.

References

Farrell M (1999) Case for children with a life-threatening disease. In: *Children and Death 4th International Conference*, Bristol, UK

Frankl V (1987) *Man's Search for Meaning: An Introduction to Logotherapy*. Hodder and Stoughton, London

Kuykendall J (1998) Oral presentation, London

11

Epilogue

On 4th June 2003, I was with my daughter and son-in-law when my second grandson came into the world. Sadly, he had died the day before. His was a life that was clearly not intended to last longer than the twenty-four weeks he spent in his mother's womb, and when we saw the extent of little David's problems, we had to acknowledge a sense of relief at the brevity of his life. Nevertheless, saying farewell to him brought a grief to our family that we had hitherto never experienced. The loss of a life that had hardly even begun to reach its potential seemed particularly poignant—and yet, as time went on, we realised that his brief existence carried a unique value that continues to enrich his family's lives.

For me, little David personified the title of this book and gave substance to my perception that every life touches other lives in some way. The impact of the tiniest pebble in the largest ocean may be almost imperceptible—yet it resonates with the cycle of creation that insists upon the interweaving of life and death with all that comes before, between and beyond.

Appendix

Recommended books for children

Crossley D (2000) *Muddles, Puddles and Sunshine.* Hawthorn Press, Stroud

Gliori D (1999) *No Matter What.* Bloomsbury, London

Hanson W (1998) *The Next Place.* Child's Play (International) Ltd, Minnesota

Ironside V (1996) *The Huge Bag of Worries.* Hodder Wayland, London

Mellonie B, Ingpen R (1997 *Beginnings and Endings with Lifetimes in between.* Belitha Press, London

Moon N (1997) *Billy's Sunflower.* Scholastic Little Hippo, London

Rock L (2004) *When Goodbye is For Ever.* Lion Publishing, Oxford

Rosen M (2004) *Sad Book.* Walker Books, London

Stickney D (1997) *Waterbugs and Dragonflies.* Continuum Books, London

Varley S (1992) *Badger's Parting Gifts.* Picture Lions, Oxford

Bibliography

Abdelnoor A, Hollins S (2004) The effect of childhood bereavement on secondary school performance. *Educ Psychol Pract* **20**: 43–54

Angus L, Levitt H, Hardtke K (1999) The narrative process coding system: research applications and implications for psychotherapy practice. *J Clin Psychol* **55**: 1255–70

Aries P (1981) *The Hour of our Death*. Allen Lane, London

Arnason A, Hafsteinsson SB (2003) The revival of death: expression, expertise and governmentality. *Br J Sociol* **54**: 43–62

Audet C, Everall RD (2003) Counsellor self-disclosure: client-informed implications for practice. *Counsel Psychother Res* **3**: 223–31

Baldwin A (2004) Psychotherapy—the new religion? *Counsel Psychother J* **15**: 9–11

Barkham M (1996) Quantitative research on psychotherapeutic interventions. In: Woolfe RD, Woolfe W, eds. *Handbook of Counselling Psychology*. Sage, London

Barnard P, Barnard I, Barnard M, Nagy J (1999) *Children, Bereavement and Trauma; Nurturing Resilience*. Jessica Kingsley Publishers, London

Bayne R, Nicholson P, Horton I (1998) *Counselling and Communication Skills for Medical Health Practitioners*. BPS Books, Leicester

Beck AT (1976) *Cognitive Therapy and the Emotional Disorders*. International Universities Press, New York

Bending M (1993) *Caring for Bereaved Children*. Cruse Bereavement Care, Richmond

Bertoia J (1993) *Drawings from a Dying Child*. Routledge, London

Black D (1998) Coping with loss: bereavement in childhood. *Br Med J* **316**: 931–33

Black D (1996) Childhood bereavement. *Br Med J* **312**: 1496

Bluebond-Langner M (1999) Children's understanding of death. In: *Children and Death 4th International Conference*, Bristol, UK

Bluebond-Langner M (1978) *The Private Worlds of Dying Children*. Princeton University Press, Princeton

Bond T (1993) *Standards and Ethics for Counselling in Action*. Sage, London

Bowlby J (1969) *Attachment and Loss*. Basic Books, New York

Bowlby J (1961) Processes of mourning. *Int J Psychoanal* **44**: 317–40

Brayne M (2003) Journalists and the stiff upper lip. *Counsel Psychother J* **14**: 8–10

Brown E (1999) *Loss, Change and Grief*. David Fulton, London

Cadranell J (1994) Talking about death—parents and children. In: Hill L, ed. *Caring for Dying Children and their Families*. Chapman and Hall, London

Casement P (1986) *On Learning from the Patient*. Tavistock Publications, London

Clare A (2000) *Masculinity in Crisis*. Chatto and Windus, London

Clark D, Seymour J (2002) *Reflections on Palliative Care*. Open University Press, Buckingham

Cobb M (2001) *The Dying Soul*. Open University Press, Buckingham

Davies AM (2001) Death of adolescents: parental grief and coping strategies. *Br J Nurs* **10**: 13–24

Davies B, Deveau E, deVeber B *et al* (1998) Experiences of mothers in five countries whose child died of cancer. *Cancer Nurs* **21**: 301–11

De Hennezel M (1997) *Intimate Death*. Warner Books, London

Denscombe M (1998) *The Good Research Guide*. Open University Press, Buckingham

Doka KJe (1995) *Children Mourning, Mourning Children*. Hospice Foundation of America, Washington

Dowling M (2000) *Young Children's Personal, Social and Emotional Development*. Sage, London

Driscoll R (1987) Ordinary language as a common language for psychotherapy. *J Integr Eclect Psychother* **6**: 184–94

Dryden W (1996) *Handbook of Individual Therapy*. Sage, London

Bibliography

Dryden W (1992) *Integrative and Eclectic Therapy*. Open University Press, Buckingham

Dryden W (1991) *A Dialogue with Arnold Lazarus*. Open University Press, Buckingham

Dyregrov A (1991) *Grief in Children*. Jessica Kingsley, London

Edwards CE, Murdock NL (1994) Characteristics of therapist self-disclosure in the counselling process. *J Counsel Devel* **72**: 384–89

Ellis A (1989) The history of cognition in psychotherapy. In: Freeman A, Simon KM, Beutler LE, Arkowitz H. eds. *Comprehensive Handbook of Cognitive Therapy*. Plenum Press, New York

Engel GL (1961) Is grief a disease? *Psychosom Med* **23**: 18–22

Exley C (2004) Review article: the sociology of dying, death and bereavement. *Sociol Health Illness* **26**: 110–22

Fairbairn G (2000) When a baby dies—a father's view. In: Dickenson D, Johnson M, Katz JS, eds. *Death, Dying and Bereavement*. Sage, London

Farrell M (1999a) In Children and Death 4th International Conference Bristol, UK

Farrell M (1999b) *Care of the Dying Child*. NT Books, London

Fiedler FE (1950) A comparison of therapeutic relationships in psychoanalytic, non-directive and Adlerian therapy. *J Counsel Psychol* **14**: 436–45

Field D, Hockey J, Small N (1997) *Death, Gender and Ethnicity*. Routledge, London

Frankl V (1987) *Man's Search for Meaning: An Introduction to Logotherapy*. Hodder and Stoughton, London

Freud S (1917) *The Complete Works of Sigmund Freud*. Hogarth Press, New York

Freud S (1910) *Five Lectures on Psycho-Analysis*. Hogarth, London

Gardner H (1993) *Frames of Mind*. Fontana, London

Gendlin MJ (1984) The client's client: The edge of awareness. In: Levant RF, Shlien M, eds. *Client-centred Therapy and the Person-centred Approach*. Praeger, New York

Gibran K (1991) *The Prophet*. Macmillan, London

Goldacre MJ (1983) Health and sickness in the community. In: Weatherall D, Ledingham J, Worrell D, eds. *Oxford Textbook of Medicine*, Vol. 1. Oxford University Press, New York

Gorer G (1965) *Death, Grief and Mourning in Contemporary Britain*. The Cresset Press, London

Hall E (1997) Editorial. *Counselling* **8**: 245

Harmon We (1992) *The Top 500 Poems*. Columbia University Press, New York

Harrington R, Harrison L (1999) Unproven assumptions about the impact of bereavement on children. *J Roy Soc Med* **92**: 230–33

Hemingway E (1929) *A Farewell to Arms*. Jonathan Cape, London

Herbert M (1996) *Supporting Bereaved and Dying Children and their Parents*. BPS Books, Leicester

Hindmarch, C. (2000) *On the Death of a Child*. Radcliffe Medical Press Ltd, Oxon.

Hindmarch C (1995) Secondary losses for siblings. *Child Care, Health Devel* **21**: 425–31

Hodgson AK, Eden OB (2003) *'Everything has Changed' — an Exploratory Study of the Experiences of Young People with Recurrent or Metastatic Cancer*. Christie Hospital NHS Trust, Manchester

Humphrey GM, Zimpfer D (1996) *Counselling for Grief and Bereavement*. Sage, London

Irwin M, Pike J (1993) Bereavement, depressive symptoms and immune function. In: Stroebe M, Stroebe W, Hansson RO, eds. *Handbook of Bereavement Theory, Research and Intervention.* University of Cambridge Press, Cambridge

Jacobs M (2002) *Psychodynamic Counselling in Action*. Sage, London

Jewett C (1982) *Helping Children Cope with Separation and Loss*. Harvard Carman Press, Boston.

Judd D (2000) Communicating with dying children. In: Dickenson D, Johnson M, Katz JS, eds. *Death, Dying and Bereavement*. Sage, London

Jupp P, Gittings C (1999) *Death in England*. Manchester University Press, Manchester

Kahn M (1997) *Between Therapist and Client*. Henry Holt and Company, New York

Kettleborough (J2000) Why will no-one talk about my lost baby? In: *Mail on Sunday*, 2.07.00, London

Klass D (1999) *The Spiritual Lives of Bereaved Parents.* Taylor Francis, Washington, DC

Klass D, Silverman P, Nickman S (1996) *Continuing Bonds.* Taylor and Francis, Philadelphia

Kopp S (1972) *If you meet the Buddha on the road, Kill Him.* Sheldon Press, London

Kubler-Ross E (1990) *To Live Until We Say Goodbye.* Prentice-Hall, New Jersey

Kubler-Ross E (1983) *On Children and Death.* Macmillan, New York

Kubler-Ross E (1970) *On Death and Dying.* Routledge, London

Kuykendall J (1998) Oral presentation. London

Lazarus AA (1995) Multimodal Counselling. In: Nelson-Jones R, ed. *The Theory and Practice of Counselling.* Cassell, London

Lazarus AA (1989) *The Practice of Multimodal Therapy.* Johns Hopkins University Press, Baltimore

Lees J (2003) Developing therapist self-understanding through research. *Counsel Psychother Res* **3**: 147–53

Lendrum S, Syme G (1992) *The Gift of Tears.* Routledge, London

Levinas E (2000) *God, Death and Time.* Stanford University Press, Stanford, Ca

Machin L (1998) Grief counselling in context: multiple roles and professional compromise. *Br J Guid Counsel* **26**: 387

Machin L, Spall R (2004) Mapping grief: a study in practice using a quantitative and qualitative approach to exploring and addressing the range of responses to loss. *Counsel Psychother Res* **4**: 9–17

Mann S (2004) 'People-work': emotion management, stress and coping. *Br J Guid Counsel* **32**: 205–21

Markova D (2000) *I will not Die an Unlived Life.* Conari Press, Boston

McCracken A, Semel M (1998) *A Broken Heart Still Beats.* Hazelden, Minnesota

McGuire A (1996) *Ethical Guidelines for Monitoring, Evaluation and Research in Counselling.* BACP, Rugby

McLeod J (1999) *Practitioner Research in Counselling.* Sage, London

McLeod J (1997) *Narrative and Psychotherapy.* Sage, London

McLeod J (1993) *An Introduction to Counselling.* Open University Press, Buckingham

McLeod J, Machin L (1998) The context of counselling: a neglected dimension of training, research and practice. *Br J Guid Counsel* **26**: 325

Mearns D (1994) *Developing Person-Centred Counselling.* Sage, London

Meier A (2002) Narrative in psychotherapy theory, practice and research: a critical review. *Counsel Psychother Res* **2**: 239–51

Meier A, Boivin M (2000) The achievement of greater selfhood: the application of theme-analysis to a case study. *Psychother Res* **10**: 57–77

Nash T (1999) A children's hospice: a place for living. In: *Children and Death 4th International Conference*, Bristol, UK

Neimeyer RA, Anderson A (2002) Meaning Reconstruction Theory. In: Thompson, N, ed. *Loss and Grief.* Palgrave, Basingstoke

Nelson-Jones R (1999) Towards cognitive/humanistic counselling . *Counselling* **10**: 913

Nelson-Jones R (1995) *The Theory and Practice of Counselling.* Cassell, London

Neuberger J (1999) *Dying Well.* Hochland and Hochland, Cheshire

Newton M (2002) *Savage Girls and Wild Boys.* Faber and Faber, London

Norcross JC, Prochaska JO (1988) A study of eclectic and integrative views revisited. *Prof Psychol: Res Pract* **19**: 170–74

Obershaw RJ (1999) In Children and Death 4th International Conference Bristol, UK

Oliviere D, Monroe B (2003) *Patient Participation in Palliative Care: A Voice for the Voiceless.* Oxford University Press, London

Papadatou D (1999) The dying adolescent. In: *Children and Death 4th International Conference*, Bristol, UK

Parkes CM (2000) Counselling bereaved people—help or harm? *Bereavement Care* **19**: 19–21

Parkes CM (1972) *Bereavement: Studies in Adult Life*. Sage, London

Parkes CM, Relf M, Couldrick A (1996) *Counselling in Terminal Care and Bereavement*. BPS Books, Leicester

Parkes CM, Shannon P, Edgeworth S (2000) Sixth International Conference on grief and bereavement in contemporary society. *Bereavement Care* **19**: 45–46

Patton MQ (1990) *Qualitative Evaluation and Research Methods*. Sage, New York

Payne S (1999) In Children and Death 4th International Conference Bristol, UK

Peberdy A (2000) Spiritual care of dying people. In: Dickenson D, Johnson M, Katz JS, eds. *Death, Dying and Bereavement*. Sage, London

Pennels M, Smith S (1995) *The Forgotten Mourners*. Jessica Kingsley, London

Piaget J (1929) *The Child's Conception of the World*. Routledge, London

Potts S (2000a) Spirituality in children's palliative care. *Pall Matters* : 4–5

Potts S (2000b) Treasure Weekend: 'Look back and keep going' In: *Child bereavement—Who Cares? Conference*, London, UK

Potts S (1999) In Children and Death 4th International Conference Bristol, UK

Potts S, Farrell M (1999) Treasure Weekend: Supporting bereaved siblings. *Pall Med* **13**: 51–56

Rando TA (1983a) *Grieving: How to go on Living When Someone You Love Dies*. Leamington Books, Lexington MA

Rando TA (1983b) An investigation of grief and adaptation in parents whose children have died from cancer. *J Paediatr Psychol* **8**: 3–20

Raphael B (1984) *The Anatomy of Bereavement*. Hutchinson, London

Raphael B, Middleton W, Martinek N, Miso V (1993) Counselling and therapy of the bereaved. In: Stroebe M, Stroebe W, Hansson

RO, eds. *Handbook of Bereavement.* Cambridge University Press, New York

Rasheed A (2001) *Death.* Al-Hidaayah Publishing, Birmingham

Rees D (2001) *Death and Bereavement.* Whurr Publishers, London

Robinson C, Jackson P (1999) *Children's Hospices: A Lifeline for Families.* Joseph Rowntree Foundation, NCB, London??

Rochford G (1991) Theory, concepts, feelings and practice: The contemplation of bereavement within a social work course. In: Lishman J, ed. *Handbook of Theory for Practice Teachers in Social Work.* Jessica Kingsley, London

Rogers C (1978) *On Personal Power.* Constable, London

Rogers C (1961) *On Becoming a Person.* Constable, London

Rosenblatt PC (2000a) *Parent Grief: Narratives of Loss and Relationship.* Brunner/Mazel, Philadelphia

Rosenblatt PC (2000b) Parents talking in the present tense about their dead child. *Bereavement Care* 19: 35–38

Rosenblatt PC (1996) Grief that does not end. In: Klass D, Silverman P, Nickman S, eds. *Continuing Bonds.* Taylor and Francis, Philadelphia

Rowa-Dewar N (2002) Do interventions make a difference to bereaved parents: a systematic review of controlled studies. *Int J Pall Nurs* 8: 452–57

Rowe D (2000) *Friends and Enemies.* Harper Collins, London

Rubin SS (1993) Death of a child. In: Stroebe M, Stroebe W, Hansson RO, eds. *Handbook of Bereavement.* Cambridge University Press, New York

Russell MD (1997) *The Sparrow.* Black Swan Books, London

Sanders CM (1995) Grief of children and parents. In: Doka KJe, ed. *Children Mourning, Mourning Children.* Taylor and Francis, Bristol, USA

Shawe Me (1992) *Enduring, Sharing, Loving.* Dartman Longman Todd, London

Sheldon F (1997) *Psychosocial Palliative Care.* Stanley Thornes, Cheltenham

Bibliography

Silverman P (1999) In Children and Death 4th International Conference, Bristol, UK

Silverman P, Nickman S (1996) Concluding thoughts. In: Klass D, Silverman P, Nickman S, eds. *Continuing Bonds.* Taylor and Francis, Philadelphia

Simpson M (1979) *Dying, Death and Grief: A Critical Bibliography.* University of Philadelphia Press, Philadelphia

Spong S, Hollanders H (2003) Cognitive therapy and social power. *Counsel Psychother Res* **3**: 216–22

Stickney D (1982) *Waterbugs and Dragonflies.* Cassell, London.

Stokes J, Crossley D (1995) Camp Winston: An intervention with bereaved children. In: Smith SC, Pennells M, eds. *Interventions with Bereaved Children.* Jessica Kingsley, London

Strauss A, Corbin J (1990) *Grounded Theory Procedures and Techniques.* Sage, London

Stroebe M (1992) Coping with Bereavement: A review of the griefwork hypothesis. *Omega* **26**: 19–42

Stroebe M, Gergen M, Gergen K, Stroebe W (1992) Broken hearts or broken bonds. *Am Psychologist* **47**: 1205–12

Stroebe M, Schut H (1998) Culture and grief. *Bereavement Care* **17**: 7–11

Stroebe M, Schut H (1995) In International Workgroup on Death, Dying and Bereavement, Oxford, UK

Stroebe M, Stroebe W, Hansson RO (1993) *Handbook of Bereavement: Theory, Research and Intervention.* Cambridge University Press, New York

The Thompson Chain-Reference Bible, New International Version, B. B. Kirkbride Bible Co, Indiana

Thorne B (1996) Person-centred counselling. In: Dryden W, ed. *Handbook of Individual Therapy.* Sage, London

Walter T (1999) *On Bereavement: The Culture of Grief.* Open University Press, Buckingham

Walter T (1996) A new model of grief: bereavement and biography. *Mortality* **1**: 7–25

Walter T (1994) *The Revival of Death.* Routledge, London

Walter T (1991) Modern death—taboo or not taboo? *Sociology* **25**: 293–310

Ward B (1995) *Good Grief.* Jessica Kingsley, London

Wass H (2004) A perspective on the current state of death education. *Death Stud* **28**: 289–308

Wheeler S (2003) Men and Therapy: are they compatible? *Counsel Psychother Res* **3**: 3–5

Wilkins P (1997) Congruence and Counter-transference: similarities and differences. *Counselling* **8**: 36–41

Wilkinson T (1991) *The Death of a Child.* Julia MacRae Books, London

Winnicott DW (1958) *Collected Papers: Through Paediatrics to Psychoanalysis.* Hogarth Press, London

Worden JW (1996) *Children and Grief.* Guildford Press, New York

Worden JW (1991) *Grief Counselling and Grief Therapy*, 2nd edn. Routledge, London

Worden JW (1988) *Grief Counselling and Grief Therapy.* Routledge, London

Wordsworth W (2000) Essays upon epitaphs. In: Dickenson D, Johnson M, Katz JS, eds. *Death, Dying and Bereavement.* Sage, London

Wortman, CB, Silver RC, Kessler RC (1999) The meaning of loss and adjustment to bereavement. In: Stroebe M, Stroebe W, Hansson RO, eds. *Handbook of Bereavement.* Cambridge University Press, Cambridge

Wortman S, Silver RC (1989) The myths of coping with loss. *J Consult Clin Psychol* **57**: 349–57

Wortman S, Silver RC, Kessler RC (1993) Adjustment to bereavement. In: Stroebe M, Stroebe W, Hanson RO, eds. *Handbook of Bereavement.* Cambridge University Press, Cambridge

Wosket V (1999) *The Therapeutic Use of Self.* Routledge, London

Yehl Marta S (2004) *Healing the Hurt, Restoring the Hope.* Rodale, London

Index

Everylife